Put a rocket under your revision with CGP!

GCSE Physics isn't the easiest subject on Earth, and that's putting it mildly.
Luckily, we've squeezed the facts, theory and practical skills you'll need into this CGP book —
plus exam practice questions to put your new-found Physics knowledge to the test.

How to access your free Online Edition

This book includes a free Online Edition to read on your PC, Mac or tablet.
To access it, just go to **cgpbooks.co.uk/extras** and enter this code...

4462 0563 1148 2085

By the way, this code only works for one person. If somebody else has used
this book before you, they might have already claimed the Online Edition.

CGP — still the best! ☺

Our sole aim here at CGP is to produce the highest quality books —
carefully written, immaculately presented and dangerously close to being funny.

Then we work our socks off to get them out to you
— at the cheapest possible prices.

Contents

Topic 6 — Waves

Topic 7 — Magnetism and Electromagnetism

Topic 8 — Space Physics

Practical Skills

Published by CGP.

From original material by Richard Parsons.

Editors: Emily Garrett, Frances Rooney, Charlotte Whiteley, Sarah Williams and Jonathan Wray.

Contributors: Paddy Gannon, Gemma Hallam and Jason Howell.

With thanks to Karen Wells and Mark A Edwards for the proofreading.

With thanks to Ana Pungartnik for the copyright research.

Printed by Elanders Ltd, Newcastle upon Tyne.
Clipart from Corel®

The Scientific Method

This section **isn't** about how to 'do' science — but it does show you the way **most scientists** work.

Scientists Come Up With Hypotheses — Then Test Them

1) Scientists try to <u>explain</u> things. They start by <u>observing</u> something they don't understand.

2) They then come up with a <u>hypothesis</u> — a possible <u>explanation</u> for what they've observed.

3) The next step is to <u>test</u> whether the hypothesis might be <u>right or not</u>. This involves making a <u>prediction</u> based on the hypothesis and testing it by <u>gathering evidence</u> (i.e. <u>data</u>) from <u>investigations</u>. If <u>evidence</u> from <u>experiments</u> backs up a prediction, you're a step closer to figuring out if the hypothesis is true.

About 100 years ago, scientists hypothesised that atoms looked like this.

Several Scientists Will Test a Hypothesis

1) Normally, scientists <u>share</u> their <u>findings</u> in <u>peer-reviewed journals</u>, or at <u>conferences</u>.

2) <u>Peer-review</u> is where <u>other scientists</u> check results and scientific explanations to make sure they're 'scientific' (e.g. that experiments have been done in a sensible way) <u>before</u> they're published. It helps to <u>detect false claims</u>, but it doesn't mean that findings are <u>correct</u> — just that they're not wrong in any <u>obvious</u> way.

3) Once other scientists have found out about a hypothesis, they'll start basing their <u>own predictions</u> on it and carry out their <u>own experiments</u>. They'll also try to <u>reproduce</u> the original experiments to <u>check the results</u> — and if all the experiments in the world <u>back up</u> the <u>hypothesis</u>, then scientists start to think the hypothesis is <u>true</u>.

4) However, if a scientist does an experiment that <u>doesn't fit</u> with the hypothesis (and other scientists can reproduce the results) then the hypothesis may need to be <u>modified</u> or <u>scrapped</u> altogether.

After more evidence was gathered, scientists changed their hypothesis to this

If All the Evidence Supports a Hypothesis, It's Accepted — For Now

1) <u>Accepted hypotheses</u> are often referred to as <u>theories</u>. Our <u>currently accepted</u> theories are the ones that have survived this 'trial by evidence' — they've been <u>tested many times</u> over the years and <u>survived</u>.

2) However, theories <u>never</u> become totally indisputable <u>fact</u>. If <u>new evidence</u> comes along that <u>can't be explained</u> using the existing theory, then the hypothesising and testing is likely to <u>start all over again</u>.

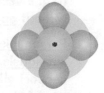

Now we think it's more like this.

Theories Can Involve Different Types of Models

1) A <u>representational model</u> is a <u>simplified description</u> or <u>picture</u> of what's going on in real life. Like all models, it can be used to <u>explain observations</u> and <u>make predictions</u>. E.g. the <u>Bohr model</u> of an atom is a simplified way of showing the arrangement of electrons in an atom (see p.43). It can be used to explain electron excitations in atoms.

Scientists test models by carrying out experiments to check that the predictions made by the model happen as expected.

2) <u>Computational models</u> use computers to make <u>simulations</u> of complex real-life processes, such as climate change. They're used when there are a <u>lot</u> of different <u>variables</u> (factors that change) to consider, and because you can easily <u>change their design</u> to take into account <u>new data</u>.

3) All models have <u>limitations</u> on what they can <u>explain</u> or <u>predict</u>. E.g. <u>the Big Bang model</u> (a model used to describe the beginning of the Universe) can be used to explain why everything in the Universe is moving away from us. One of its limitations is that it <u>doesn't explain</u> the moments before the Big Bang.

I'm off to the zoo to test my hippo-thesis...

The scientific method has been developed over time. Aristotle (an Ancient Greek philosopher) was the first person to realise that theories needed to be based on observations. Muslim scholars then introduced the ideas of creating a hypothesis, testing it, and repeating your work to check your results. And a chap called Roger Bacon later developed things further by writing down everything he did, so other scientists could try to reproduce his work.

Communication & Issues Created by Science

Scientific developments can be great, but they can sometimes <u>raise more questions</u> than they answer...

It's Important to Communicate Scientific Discoveries to the General Public

Some scientific discoveries show that people should <u>change their habits</u>, or they might provide ideas that could be <u>developed</u> into new <u>technology</u>. So scientists need to <u>tell the world</u> about their discoveries.

<u>Radioactive materials</u> are used widely in <u>medicine</u> for <u>imaging</u> and <u>treatment</u> (see p.48). Information about these materials needs to be communicated to <u>doctors</u> so they can <u>make use</u> of them, and to <u>patients</u>, so they can make <u>informed decisions</u> about their <u>treatment</u>.

Scientific Evidence can be Presented in a Biased Way

1) Scientific discoveries that are reported in the <u>media</u> (e.g. newspapers or television) <u>aren't</u> peer-reviewed.

2) This means that, even though news stories are often <u>based</u> on data that has been peer-reviewed, the data might be <u>presented</u> in a way that is <u>over-simplified</u> or <u>inaccurate</u>, making it open to <u>misinterpretation</u>.

3) People who want to make a point can sometimes <u>present data</u> in a <u>biased way</u>. (Sometimes <u>without knowing</u> they're doing it.) For example, a scientist might overemphasise a relationship in the data, or a newspaper article might describe details of data <u>supporting</u> an idea without giving any evidence <u>against</u> it.

Scientific Developments are Great, but they can Raise Issues

Scientific <u>knowledge is increased</u> by doing experiments. And this knowledge leads to <u>scientific developments</u>, e.g. new technologies or new advice. These developments can create <u>issues</u> though. For example:

<u>Economic issues:</u> Society <u>can't</u> always <u>afford</u> to do things scientists recommend (e.g. investing in alternative energy sources) without <u>cutting back elsewhere</u>.

<u>Personal issues:</u> Some decisions will affect <u>individuals</u>. For example, someone might support <u>alternative energy</u>, but object if a <u>wind farm</u> is built next to their house.

<u>Social issues:</u> Decisions based on scientific evidence affect <u>people</u> — e.g. should fossil fuels be taxed more highly? <u>Would the effect on people's lifestyles be acceptable...</u>

<u>Environmental issues:</u> <u>Human activity</u> often affects the <u>natural environment</u>. For example, building a <u>dam</u> to produce electricity will change the <u>local habitat</u> so some species might be displaced. But it will also reduce our need for <u>fossil fuels</u>, so will help to reduce <u>climate change</u>.

Science Can't Answer Every Question — Especially Ethical Ones

1) We don't <u>understand everything</u>. We're always finding out <u>more</u>, but we'll never know <u>all</u> the answers.

2) In order to answer scientific questions, scientists need <u>data</u> to provide <u>evidence</u> for their hypotheses.

3) Some questions can't be answered <u>yet</u> because the data <u>can't</u> currently be <u>collected</u>, or because there's <u>not enough</u> data to <u>support</u> a theory.

4) <u>Eventually</u>, as we get <u>more evidence</u>, we'll answer some of the questions that <u>currently</u> can't be answered, e.g. what the impact of global warming on sea levels will be. But there will always be the "<u>Should we be doing this at all?</u>"-type questions that experiments <u>can't</u> help us to answer...

Think about <u>new drugs which can be taken to boost your 'brain power'</u>.

THE GAZETTE
BRAIN-BOOSTING DRUGS MAKE A MOCKERY OF EXAMS

THE POST
GENIUS PILLS TO BECOME THE NEW COFFEE

- Some people think they're <u>good</u> as they could improve concentration or memory. New drugs could let people think in ways beyond the powers of normal brains.

- Other people say they're <u>bad</u> — they could give you an <u>unfair advantage</u> in exams. And people might be <u>pressured</u> into taking them so that they could work more <u>effectively</u>, and for <u>longer hours</u>.

Tea to milk or milk to tea? — Totally unanswerable by science...

Science can't tell you whether or not you should do something. That's for you and society to decide. But there are tons of questions science might be able to answer, like where life came from and where my superhero socks are.

Risk

By reading this page you are agreeing to the <u>risk</u> of a paper cut or severe drowsiness...

Nothing is Completely Risk-Free

1) A <u>hazard</u> is something that could <u>potentially cause harm</u>.

2) All hazards have a <u>risk</u> attached to them — this is the <u>chance</u> that the hazard will cause harm.

3) The risks of some things seem pretty <u>obvious</u>, or we've known about them for a while, like the risk of causing <u>acid rain</u> by polluting the atmosphere, or of having a <u>car accident</u> when you're travelling in a car.

4) <u>New technology</u> arising from <u>scientific advances</u> can bring <u>new risks</u>, e.g. scientists are unsure whether <u>nanoparticles</u> that are being used in cosmetics and suncream might be harming the cells in our bodies. These risks need to be considered <u>alongside</u> the <u>benefits</u> of the technology, e.g. improved sun protection.

5) You can estimate the <u>size</u> of a risk based on <u>how many times</u> something happens in a big sample (e.g. 100 000 people) over a given <u>period</u> (e.g. a year). For example, you could assess the risk of a driver crashing by recording how many people in a group of 100 000 drivers crashed their cars over a year.

6) To make a <u>decision</u> about an activity that involves a <u>risk</u>, we need to take into account the <u>chance</u> of the risk happening and how <u>serious</u> the <u>consequences</u> would be if it did. So if an activity involves a risk that's <u>very likely</u> to happen, with <u>serious consequences</u> if it does, that activity is considered <u>high risk</u>.

People Make Their Own Decisions About Risk

1) Not all risks have the same <u>consequences</u>, e.g. if you chop veg with a sharp knife you risk cutting your finger, but if you go scuba-diving you risk death. You're much <u>more likely</u> to cut your finger during half an hour of <u>chopping</u> than to die during half an hour of <u>scuba-diving</u>. But most people are happier to accept a higher <u>probability</u> of an accident if the <u>consequences</u> are <u>short-lived</u> and fairly <u>minor</u>.

2) People tend to be more willing to accept a risk if they <u>choose</u> to do something (e.g. go scuba diving), compared to having the risk <u>imposed</u> on them (e.g. having a nuclear power station built next door).

3) People's <u>perception</u> of risk (how risky they <u>think</u> something is) isn't always <u>accurate</u>. They tend to view <u>familiar</u> activities as <u>low-risk</u> and <u>unfamiliar</u> activities as <u>high-risk</u> — even if that's not the case. For example, cycling on roads is often <u>high-risk</u>, but many people are happy to do it because it's a <u>familiar</u> activity. Air travel is actually pretty <u>safe</u>, but a lot of people perceive it as <u>high-risk</u>.

4) People may <u>underestimate</u> the risk of things with <u>long-term</u> or <u>invisible</u> effects, e.g. using tanning beds.

Investigations Can be Hazardous

1) Hazards from science experiments might include:

Hmm... why is this laser not working?

- <u>Lasers</u>, e.g. if a laser is directed into the eye, this can cause blindness.
- <u>Gamma radiation</u>, e.g. gamma-emitting radioactive sources can cause cancer.
- <u>Fire</u>, e.g. an unattended Bunsen burner is a fire hazard.
- <u>Electricity</u>, e.g. faulty electrical equipment could give you a shock.

2) Part of planning an investigation is making sure that it's <u>safe</u>.

3) You should always make sure that you <u>identify</u> all the hazards that you might encounter. Then you should think of ways of <u>reducing the risks</u> from the hazards you've identified. For example:

- If you're working with <u>springs</u>, always wear safety goggles. This will reduce the risk of the spring hitting your eye if the spring snaps.
- If you're using a <u>Bunsen burner</u>, stand it on a heat proof mat. This will reduce the risk of starting a fire.

You can find out about potential hazards by looking in textbooks, doing some internet research, or asking your teacher.

Not revising — an unacceptable exam hazard...

The world's a dangerous place, but if you can recognise hazards, decide how to reduce their risks, and be happy to accept some risks, you can still have fun. Just maybe don't go skydiving with a great white shark on Friday 13th.

Designing Investigations

Dig out your lab coat and dust down your badly-scratched safety goggles... it's <u>investigation time</u>.

Investigations Produce Evidence to Support or Disprove a Hypothesis

1) Scientists <u>observe</u> things and come up with <u>hypotheses</u> to test them (see p.1).
   You need to be able to do the same. For example:

   > <u>Observation</u>: People have big feet and spots. <u>Hypothesis</u>: Having big feet causes spots.

2) To <u>determine</u> whether or not a hypothesis is <u>right</u>, you need to do an <u>investigation</u> to gather evidence. To do this, you need to use your hypothesis to make a <u>prediction</u> — something you think <u>will happen</u> that you can test. E.g. people who have bigger feet will have more spots.

3) Investigations are used to see if there are <u>patterns</u> or <u>relationships</u> between <u>two variables</u>, e.g. to see if there's a pattern or relationship between the variables 'number of spots' and 'size of feet'.

Evidence Needs to be Repeatable, Reproducible and Valid

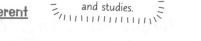
Investigations include experiments and studies.

1) <u>Repeatable</u> means that if the <u>same person</u> does an experiment again using the <u>same methods</u> and equipment, they'll get <u>similar results</u>.

2) <u>Reproducible</u> means that if <u>someone else</u> does the experiment, or a <u>different</u> method or piece of equipment is used, the results will still be <u>similar</u>.

3) If data is <u>repeatable</u> and <u>reproducible</u>, it's <u>reliable</u> and scientists are more likely to <u>have confidence</u> in it.

4) <u>Valid results</u> are both repeatable and reproducible AND they <u>answer the original question</u>. They come from experiments that were designed to be a FAIR TEST...

To Make an Investigation a Fair Test You Have to Control the Variables

1) In a lab experiment you usually <u>change one variable</u> and <u>measure</u> how it affects <u>another variable</u>.

2) To make it a fair test, <u>everything else</u> that could affect the results should <u>stay the same</u> — otherwise you can't tell if the thing you're changing is causing the results or not.

3) The variable you CHANGE is called the INDEPENDENT variable.

4) The variable you MEASURE when you change the independent variable is the DEPENDENT variable.

5) The variables that you KEEP THE SAME are called CONTROL variables.

> You could find how <u>current</u> through a circuit component affects the <u>potential difference</u> across the component by measuring the <u>potential difference</u> at different currents. The <u>independent variable</u> is the <u>current</u>. The <u>dependent variable</u> is the <u>potential difference</u>. <u>Control variables</u> include the <u>temperature</u> of the component, the <u>p.d.</u> of the power supply, etc.

6) Because you can't always control all the variables, you often need to use a <u>control experiment</u>. This is an experiment that's kept under the <u>same conditions</u> as the rest of the investigation, but <u>doesn't</u> have anything <u>done</u> to it. This is so that you can see what happens when you don't change anything at all.

The Bigger the Sample Size the Better

1) Data based on <u>small samples</u> isn't as good as data based on large samples. A sample should <u>represent</u> the <u>whole population</u> (i.e. it should share as many of the characteristics in the population as possible) — a small sample can't do that as well. It's also harder to spot <u>anomalies</u> if your sample size is too small.

2) The <u>bigger</u> the sample size the <u>better</u>, but scientists have to be <u>realistic</u> when choosing how big. For example, if you were studying the effects of <u>living</u> near a <u>nuclear power plant</u>, it'd be great to study <u>everyone</u> who lived near a nuclear power plant (a huge sample), but it'd take ages and cost a bomb. It's more realistic to study a thousand people, with a range of ages, gender, and race.

This is no high street survey — it's a designer investigation...

Not only do you need to be able to plan your own investigations, you should also be able to look at someone else's plan and decide whether or not it needs improving. Those examiners aren't half demanding.

Collecting Data

You've designed the perfect investigation — now it's time to get your hands mucky and collect some data.

Your Data Should be Repeatable, Reproducible, Accurate and Precise

1) To check repeatability you need to repeat the readings and check that the results are similar. You need to repeat each reading at least three times.

2) To make sure your results are reproducible you can cross check them by taking a second set of readings with another instrument (or a different observer).

3) Your data also needs to be ACCURATE. Really accurate results are those that are really close to the true answer. The accuracy of your results usually depends on your method — you need to make sure you're measuring the right thing and that you don't miss anything that should be included in the measurements. E.g. estimating the volume of an irregularly shaped solid by measuring the sides isn't very accurate because this will not take into account any gaps in the object. It's more accurate to measure the volume using a eureka can (see p.105).

Brian's result was a curate.

Repeat	Data set 1	Data set 2
1	12	11
2	14	17
3	13	14
Mean	13	14

Data set 1 is more precise than data set 2.

4) Your data also needs to be PRECISE. Precise results are ones where the data is all really close to the mean (average) of your repeated results (i.e. not spread out).

Your Equipment has to be Right for the Job

1) The measuring equipment you use has to be sensitive enough to measure the changes you're looking for. For example, if you need to measure changes of 1 cm^3 you need to use a measuring cylinder or burette that can measure in 1 cm^3 steps — it'd be no good trying with one that only measures 10 cm^3 steps.

2) The smallest change a measuring instrument can detect is called its RESOLUTION. E.g. some mass balances have a resolution of 1 g, some have a resolution of 0.1 g, and some are even more sensitive.

3) Also, equipment needs to be calibrated by measuring a known value. If there's a difference between the measured and known value, you can use this to correct the inaccuracy of the equipment.

You Need to Look out for Errors and Anomalous Results

1) The results of your experiment will always vary a bit because of RANDOM ERRORS — unpredictable differences caused by things like human errors in measuring. The errors when you make a reading from a ruler are random. You have to estimate or round the distance when it's between two marks — so sometimes your figure will be a bit above the real one, and sometimes it will be a bit below.

2) You can reduce the effect of random errors by taking repeat readings and finding the mean. This will make your results more precise.

3) If a measurement is wrong by the same amount every time, it's called a SYSTEMATIC ERROR. For example, if you measured from the very end of your ruler instead of from the 0 cm mark every time, all your measurements would be a bit small. Repeating the experiment in the exact same way and calculating a mean won't correct a systematic error.

If there's no systematic error, then doing repeats and calculating a mean could make your results more accurate.

4) Just to make things more complicated, if a systematic error is caused by using equipment that isn't zeroed properly, it's called a ZERO ERROR. For example, if a mass balance always reads 1 gram before you put anything on it, all your measurements will be 1 gram too heavy.

5) You can compensate for some systematic errors if you know about them though, e.g. if your mass balance always reads 1 gram before you put anything on it you can subtract 1 gram from all your results.

6) Sometimes you get a result that doesn't fit in with the rest at all. This is called an ANOMALOUS RESULT. You should investigate it and try to work out what happened. If you can work out what happened (e.g. you measured something totally wrong) you can ignore it when processing your results.

Watch what you say to that mass balance — it's very sensitive...

Weirdly, data can be really precise but not very accurate. For example, a fancy piece of lab equipment might give results that are really precise, but if it's not been calibrated properly those results won't be accurate.

Processing and Presenting Data

Processing your data means doing some <u>calculations</u> with it to make it <u>more useful</u>. Once you've done that, you can present your results in a nice <u>chart</u> or <u>graph</u> to help you <u>spot any patterns</u> in your data.

Data Needs to be Organised

1) Tables are dead useful for <u>organising data</u>.
2) When you draw a table <u>use a ruler</u> and make sure <u>each column</u> has a <u>heading</u> (including the <u>units</u>).

You Might Have to Process Your Data

1) When you've done repeats of an experiment you should always calculate the <u>mean</u> (average). To do this <u>add together</u> all the data values and <u>divide</u> by the total number of values in the sample.
2) You can also find the <u>mode</u> of your results — this is the <u>value</u> that <u>occurs</u> the <u>most</u> in your set of results.
3) The <u>median</u> can be found by writing your results in numerical <u>order</u> — the median is the <u>middle number</u>.

> Ignore anomalous results when calculating the mean, mode and median.

EXAMPLE: The results of an experiment show the extension of two springs when a force is applied to both of them. Calculate the mean, mode and median of the extension for both springs.

Spring	Repeat (cm)					Mean (cm)	Mode (cm)	Median (cm)
	1	2	3	4	5			
A	18	26	22	26	28	(18 + 26 + 22 + 26 + 28) ÷ 5 = 24	26	26
B	11	14	20	15	20	(11 + 14 + 20 + 15 + 20) ÷ 5 = 16	20	15

Round to the Lowest Number of Significant Figures

The <u>first significant figure</u> of a number is the first digit that's <u>not zero</u>. The second and third significant figures come <u>straight after</u> (even if they're zeros). You should be aware of significant figures in calculations.

1) In <u>any</u> calculation, you should round to the <u>lowest number of significant figures</u> (s.f.) given.
2) Remember to write down <u>how many</u> significant figures you've rounded to after your answer.
3) If your calculation has multiple steps, <u>only</u> round the <u>final</u> answer, or it won't be as accurate.

EXAMPLE: The mass of a solid is 0.24 g and its volume is 0.715 cm³. Calculate the density of the solid.

Density = 0.24 g ÷ 0.715 cm³ = 0.33566... = 0.34 g/cm³ (2 s.f.)

2 s.f.   3 s.f.   Final answer should be rounded to 2 s.f.

If Your Data Comes in Categories, Present It in a Bar Chart

1) If the independent variable is <u>categoric</u> (comes in distinct categories, e.g. solid, liquid, gas) you should use a <u>bar chart</u> to display the data.
2) You also use them if the independent variable is <u>discrete</u> (the data can be counted in chunks, where there's no in-between value, e.g. number of protons is discrete because you can't have half a proton).
3) There are some <u>golden rules</u> you need to follow for <u>drawing</u> bar charts:

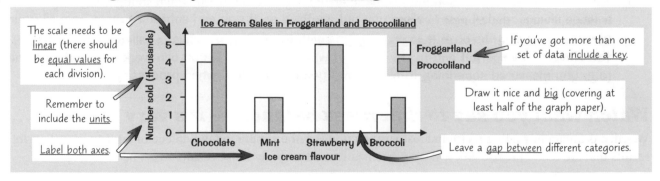

The scale needs to be <u>linear</u> (there should be <u>equal values</u> for each division).

Remember to include the <u>units</u>.

<u>Label both axes</u>.

Ice Cream Sales in Froggartland and Broccoliland

Number sold (thousands) — Ice cream flavour — Chocolate, Mint, Strawberry, Broccoli

Froggartland / Broccoliland

If you've got more than one set of data <u>include a key</u>.

Draw it nice and <u>big</u> (covering at least half of the graph paper).

Leave a <u>gap between</u> different categories.

If Your Data is Continuous, Plot a Graph

If both variables are <u>continuous</u> (numerical data that can have any value within a range, e.g. length, volume, temperature) you should use a <u>graph</u> to display the data.

Here are the rules for plotting points on a graph:

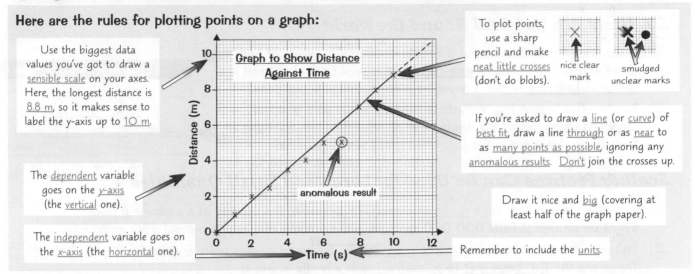

Use the biggest data values you've got to draw a <u>sensible scale</u> on your axes. Here, the longest distance is <u>8.8 m</u>, so it makes sense to label the y-axis up to <u>10 m</u>.

The <u>dependent</u> variable goes on the <u>y-axis</u> (the <u>vertical</u> one).

The <u>independent</u> variable goes on the <u>x-axis</u> (the <u>horizontal</u> one).

To plot points, use a sharp pencil and make <u>neat little crosses</u> (don't do blobs). nice clear mark / smudged unclear marks

If you're asked to draw a <u>line</u> (or <u>curve</u>) of <u>best fit</u>, draw a line <u>through</u> or as <u>near</u> to as <u>many points as possible</u>, ignoring any <u>anomalous results</u>. <u>Don't</u> join the crosses up.

Draw it nice and <u>big</u> (covering at least half of the graph paper).

Remember to include the <u>units</u>.

Graphs Can Give You a Lot of Information About Your Data

1) The <u>gradient</u> (slope) of a graph tells you how quickly the <u>dependent variable</u> changes if you change the <u>independent variable</u>.

$$\text{gradient} = \frac{\text{change in } y}{\text{change in } x}$$

You can use this method to calculate other rates from a graph, so long as you always make x time.

This <u>graph</u> shows the <u>distance travelled</u> by a vehicle against <u>time</u>. The graph is <u>linear</u> (it's a straight line graph), so you can simply calculate the <u>gradient</u> of the line to find out the <u>speed</u> of the vehicle.

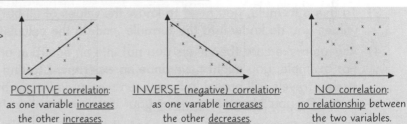

1) To calculate the gradient, pick <u>two points</u> on the line that are easy to read and a <u>good distance</u> apart.

2) <u>Draw a line down</u> from one of the points and a <u>line across</u> from the other to make a <u>triangle</u>. The line drawn down the side of the triangle is the <u>change in y</u> and the line across the bottom is the <u>change in x</u>.

Change in y = 6.8 – 2.0 = 4.8 m   Change in x = 5.2 – 1.6 = 3.6 s

$$\text{Rate} = \text{gradient} = \frac{\text{change in } y}{\text{change in } x} = \frac{4.8 \text{ m}}{3.6 \text{ s}} = \underline{1.3 \text{ m/s}}$$

The units of the gradient are (units of y)/(units of x).

2) To find the <u>gradient of a curve</u> at a <u>certain point</u>, draw a <u>tangent</u> to the curve at that point. This is a <u>straight line</u> that <u>touches</u> the curve at that <u>point</u>, but doesn't <u>cross</u> it. Then just find the <u>gradient of the tangent</u> in the same way as above.

tangent / point / curve

3) The <u>intercept</u> of a graph is where the line of best fit crosses one of the <u>axes</u>. The <u>x-intercept</u> is where the line of best fit crosses the x-axis and the <u>y-intercept</u> is where it crosses the <u>y-axis</u>.

Graphs Show the Relationship Between Two Variables

1) You can get <u>three</u> types of <u>correlation</u> (relationship) between variables:

2) Just because there's correlation, it doesn't mean the change in one variable is <u>causing</u> the change in the other — there might be <u>other factors</u> involved (see page 9).

<u>POSITIVE</u> correlation: as one variable <u>increases</u> the other <u>increases</u>.

<u>INVERSE</u> (negative) correlation: as one variable <u>increases</u> the other <u>decreases</u>.

<u>NO</u> correlation: <u>no relationship</u> between the two variables.

I love eating apples — I call it core elation...

Science is all about finding relationships between things. And I don't mean that chemists gather together in corners to discuss whether or not Devini and Sebastian might be a couple... though they probably do that too.

Units and Equations

Graphs and maths skills are all very well, but the numbers don't mean much if you can't get the <u>units</u> right.

S.I. Units Are Used All Round the World

1) It wouldn't be all that useful if I defined volume in terms of <u>bath tubs</u>, you defined it in terms of <u>egg-cups</u> and my pal Sarwat defined it in terms of <u>balloons</u> — we'd never be able to compare our data.

2) To stop this happening, scientists have come up with a set of <u>standard units</u>, called S.I. units, that all scientists use to measure their data. Here are some S.I. units you'll see in physics:

Quantity	S.I. Base Unit
mass	kilogram, kg
length	metre, m
time	second, s
temperature	kelvin, K

Scaling Prefixes Can Be Used for Large and Small Quantities

1) Quantities come in a huge <u>range</u> of sizes. For example, the volume of a swimming pool might be around 2 000 000 000 cm³, while the volume of a cup is around 250 cm³.

2) To make the size of numbers more <u>manageable</u>, larger or smaller units are used. These are the <u>S.I. base unit</u> (e.g. metres) with a <u>prefix</u> in front:

prefix	tera (T)	giga (G)	mega (M)	kilo (k)	deci (d)	centi (c)	milli (m)	micro (μ)	nano (n)
multiple of unit	10^{12}	10^9	1 000 000 (10^6)	1000	0.1	0.01	0.001	0.000001 (10^{-6})	10^{-9}

3) These <u>prefixes</u> tell you <u>how much bigger</u> or <u>smaller</u> a unit is than the base unit. So one <u>kilometre</u> is <u>one thousand</u> metres.

The conversion factor is the number of times the smaller unit goes into the larger unit.

4) To <u>swap</u> from one unit to another, all you need to know is what number you have to divide or multiply by to get from the original unit to the new unit — this is called the <u>conversion factor</u>.

- To go from a <u>bigger unit</u> (like m) to a <u>smaller unit</u> (like cm), you <u>multiply</u> by the conversion factor.
- To go from a <u>smaller unit</u> (like g) to a <u>bigger unit</u> (like kg), you <u>divide</u> by the conversion factor.

5) Here are some conversions that'll be useful for GCSE physics:

Mass can have units of kg and g.
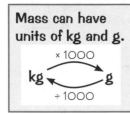

Energy can have units of J and kJ.
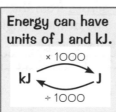

Volume can have units of m³ and cm³.
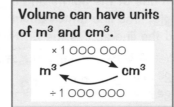

Density can have units of kg/m³ and g/cm³.
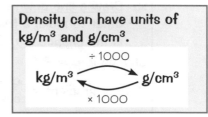

Always Check The Values Used in Equations Have the Right Units

1) Formulas and equations show <u>relationships</u> between <u>variables</u>.

2) To <u>rearrange</u> an equation, make sure that whatever you do to <u>one side</u> of the equation you also do to the <u>other side</u>.

You can find the <u>speed</u> of a wave using the equation: wave speed = frequency × wavelength. You can <u>rearrange</u> this equation to find the <u>frequency</u> by <u>dividing each side</u> by wavelength to give: frequency = wave speed ÷ wavelength.

3) To use a formula, you need to know the values of <u>all but one</u> of the variables. <u>Substitute</u> the values you do know into the formula, and do the calculation to work out the final variable.

4) Always make sure the values you put into an equation or formula have the <u>right units</u>. For example, you might have done an experiment to find the speed of a trolley. The distance the trolley travels will probably have been measured in cm, but the equation to find speed uses distance in m. So you'll have to <u>convert</u> your distance from cm to m before you put it into the equation.

5) To make sure your units are <u>correct</u>, it can help to write down the <u>units</u> on each line of your <u>calculation</u>.

I wasn't sure I liked units, but now I'm converted...

It's easy to get in a muddle when converting between units, but there's a handy way to check you've done it right. If you're moving from a smaller unit to a larger unit (e.g. g to kg) the number should get smaller, and vice versa.

Drawing Conclusions

Congratulations — you're nearly at the end of a gruelling investigation, time to <u>draw conclusions</u>.

You Can Only Conclude What the Data Shows and NO MORE

1) Drawing conclusions might seem pretty straightforward — you just <u>look at your data</u> and <u>say what pattern or relationship you see</u> between the dependent and independent variables.

> The table on the right shows the potential difference across a light bulb for three <u>different</u> currents through the bulb:

Current (A)	Potential difference (V)
6	4
9	10
12	13

> <u>CONCLUSION</u>:
> A <u>higher current</u> through the bulb gives a higher <u>potential difference</u> across the bulb.

2) But you've got to be really careful that your conclusion <u>matches the data</u> you've got and <u>doesn't go any further</u>.

> You <u>can't</u> conclude that the potential difference across <u>any circuit component</u> will be higher for a larger current — the results might be completely different.

3) You also need to be able to <u>use your results</u> to <u>justify your conclusion</u> (i.e. back up your conclusion with some specific data).

> The potential difference across the bulb was <u>9 V higher</u> with a current of 12 A compared to a current of 6 A.

4) When writing a conclusion you need to <u>refer back</u> to the original hypothesis and say whether the data <u>supports it</u> or not:

> The hypothesis for this experiment might have been that a higher current through the bulb would <u>increase</u> the potential difference across the bulb. If so, the data <u>supports</u> the hypothesis.

Correlation DOES NOT Mean Cause

If two things are correlated (i.e. there's a relationship between them) it <u>doesn't</u> necessarily mean a change in one variable is <u>causing</u> the change in the other — this is <u>**REALLY IMPORTANT**</u> — <u>**DON'T FORGET IT**</u>. There are <u>three possible reasons</u> for a correlation:

1) <u>CHANCE</u>: It might seem strange, but two things can show a correlation purely due to <u>chance</u>.

> For example, one study might find a correlation between people's hair colour and how good they are at frisbee. But other scientists <u>don't</u> get a correlation when they investigate it — the results of the first study are just a <u>fluke</u>.

2) <u>LINKED BY A 3RD VARIABLE</u>: A lot of the time it may <u>look</u> as if a change in one variable is causing a change in the other, but it <u>isn't</u> — a <u>third variable links</u> the two things.

> For example, there's a correlation between <u>water temperature</u> and <u>shark attacks</u>. This isn't because warmer water makes sharks crazy. Instead, they're linked by a third variable — the <u>number of people swimming</u> (more people swim when the water's hotter, and with more people in the water you get more shark attacks).

3) <u>CAUSE</u>: Sometimes a change in one variable does <u>cause</u> a change in the other. You can only conclude that a correlation is due to cause when you've <u>controlled all the variables</u> that could, just could, be affecting the result.

> For example, there's a correlation between <u>smoking</u> and <u>lung cancer</u>. This is because chemicals in tobacco smoke cause lung cancer. This conclusion was only made once <u>other variables</u> (such as age and exposure to other things that cause cancer) had been <u>controlled</u> and shown <u>not</u> to affect people's risk of getting lung cancer.

I conclude that this page is a bit dull...

...although, just because I find it dull doesn't mean that I can conclude it's dull (you might think it's the most interesting thing since that kid got his head stuck in the railings near school). In the exams you could be given a conclusion and asked whether some data supports it — so make sure you understand how far conclusions can go.

Uncertainties and Evaluations

Hurrah! The end of another investigation. Well, now you have to work out all the things you did <u>wrong</u>.

Uncertainty is the Amount of Error Your Measurements Might Have

1) When you <u>repeat</u> a measurement, you often get a <u>slightly different</u> figure each time you do it due to <u>random error</u>. This means that <u>each result</u> has some <u>uncertainty</u> to it.

2) The measurements you make will also have some uncertainty in them due to <u>limits</u> in the <u>resolution</u> of the equipment you use (see page 5).

3) This all means that the <u>mean</u> of a set of results will also have some uncertainty to it. You can calculate the uncertainty of a <u>mean result</u> using the equation:

4) The <u>larger</u> the range, the <u>less precise</u> your results are and the <u>more uncertainty</u> there will be in your results. Uncertainties are shown using the '±' symbol.

> The range is the largest value minus the smallest value.

$$\text{uncertainty} = \frac{\text{range}}{2}$$

**EXAMPLE:** The table below shows the results of a trolley experiment to determine the speed of the trolley as it moves along a horizontal surface. Calculate the uncertainty of the mean.

Repeat	1	2	3	mean
Speed (m/s)	2.01	1.98	2.00	2.00

1) First work out the range:

   Range = 2.01 − 1.98 = 0.030 m/s

2) Use the range to find the uncertainty:

Uncertainty = range ÷ 2 = 0.030 ÷ 2 = 0.015 m/s   So the uncertainty of the mean = 2.00 ± 0.015 m/s

5) Measuring a <u>greater amount</u> of something helps to <u>reduce uncertainty</u>. For example, in a speed experiment, measuring the distance travelled over a <u>longer period</u> compared to a shorter period will <u>reduce</u> the <u>percentage uncertainty</u> in your results.

Evaluations — Describe How it Could be Improved

An evaluation is a <u>critical analysis</u> of the whole investigation.

1) You should comment on the <u>method</u> — was it <u>valid</u>? Did you control all the other variables to make it a <u>fair test</u>?

2) Comment on the <u>quality</u> of the <u>results</u> — was there <u>enough evidence</u> to reach a valid <u>conclusion</u>? Were the results <u>repeatable</u>, <u>reproducible</u>, <u>accurate</u> and <u>precise</u>?

3) Were there any <u>anomalous</u> results? If there were <u>none</u> then <u>say so</u>. If there were any, try to <u>explain</u> them — were they caused by <u>errors</u> in measurement? Were there any other <u>variables</u> that could have <u>affected</u> the results? You should comment on the level of <u>uncertainty</u> in your results too.

4) All this analysis will allow you to say how <u>confident</u> you are that your conclusion is <u>right</u>.

5) Then you can suggest any <u>changes</u> to the <u>method</u> that would <u>improve</u> the quality of the results, so that you could have <u>more confidence</u> in your conclusion. For example, you might suggest <u>changing</u> the way you controlled a variable, or <u>increasing</u> the number of <u>measurements</u> you took. Taking more measurements at <u>narrower intervals</u> could give you a <u>more accurate result</u>. For example:

> <u>Springs</u> have a <u>limit of proportionality</u> (a maximum force before force and extension are no longer proportional). Say you use several <u>identical</u> springs to do an experiment to find the limit of proportionality of the springs. If you apply forces of 1 N, 2 N, 3 N, 4 N and 5 N, and from the results see that it is somewhere <u>between 4 N and 5 N</u>, you could <u>repeat</u> the experiment with one of the other springs, taking <u>more measurements between 4 N and 5 N</u> to get a <u>more accurate</u> value for the limit of proportionality.

6) You could also make more <u>predictions</u> based on your conclusion, then <u>further experiments</u> could be carried out to test them.

> When suggesting improvements to the investigation, always make sure that you say why you think this would make the results better.

Evaluation — next time, I'll make sure I don't burn the lab down...

So there you have it — Working Scientifically. Make sure you know this stuff like the back of your hand. It's not just in the lab that you'll need to know how to work scientifically. You can be asked about it in the exams as well.

Energy Stores and Systems

Energy is <u>never used up</u>. Instead it's just <u>transferred</u> between different <u>energy stores</u> and different objects...

Energy is Transferred Between Stores

When energy is <u>transferred</u> to an object, the energy is <u>stored</u> in one of the object's <u>energy stores</u>.

The <u>energy stores</u> you need to know are:

1) <u>Thermal</u> energy stores
2) <u>Kinetic</u> energy stores
3) <u>Gravitational potential</u> energy stores
4) <u>Elastic potential</u> energy stores
5) <u>Chemical</u> energy stores
6) <u>Magnetic</u> energy stores
7) <u>Electrostatic</u> energy stores
8) <u>Nuclear</u> energy stores

Energy is transferred <u>mechanically</u> (by a <u>force doing work</u>), <u>electrically</u> (work done by <u>moving charges</u>), by <u>heating</u> or by <u>radiation</u> (e.g. <u>light</u>, p.76, or <u>sound</u>, p.88).

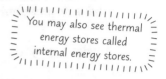

You may also see thermal energy stores called internal energy stores.

When a System Changes, Energy is Transferred

1) A <u>system</u> is just a fancy word for a <u>single</u> object (e.g. the air in a piston) or a <u>group</u> of <u>objects</u> (e.g. two colliding vehicles) that you're interested in.

2) When a system <u>changes</u>, <u>energy is transferred</u>. It can be transferred <u>into</u> or <u>away from</u> the system, between <u>different objects</u> in the system or between <u>different types</u> of energy stores.

3) <u>Closed systems</u> are systems where neither <u>matter nor energy can enter or leave</u>. The <u>net change</u> in the <u>total energy</u> of a <u>closed system</u> is <u>always zero</u>.

Energy can be Transferred by Heating...

1) Take the example of <u>boiling water</u> in a <u>kettle</u> — you can think of the <u>water</u> as the <u>system</u>. Energy is <u>transferred to</u> the water (from the kettle's heating element) <u>by heating</u>, into the water's <u>thermal</u> energy store (causing the <u>temperature</u> of the water to <u>rise</u>).

2) You could also think of the <u>kettle's</u> heating element and the <u>water</u> together as a <u>two-object system</u>. Energy is transferred <u>electrically</u> to the <u>thermal</u> energy store of the kettle's heating element, which transfers energy <u>by heating</u> to the water's <u>thermal</u> energy store.

...or by Doing Work

1) <u>Work done</u> is just another way of saying <u>energy transferred</u> — they're the <u>same thing</u>.

2) <u>Work</u> can be done <u>when current flows</u> (work is done <u>against resistance</u> in a <u>circuit</u>, see p.24) or by a <u>force</u> moving an object (there's more on this on page 53).

The <u>initial force</u> exerted by a person to <u>throw</u> a ball <u>upwards</u> does <u>work</u>. It causes an energy transfer <u>from</u> the <u>chemical energy store</u> of the person's arm to the <u>kinetic</u> energy store of the ball and arm.

A ball <u>dropped</u> from a height is accelerated by <u>gravity</u>. The <u>gravitational force</u> does <u>work</u>. It causes energy to be transferred from the ball's <u>gravitational potential</u> energy store to its <u>kinetic</u> energy store.

gravitational force

The <u>friction</u> between a car's <u>brakes</u> and its <u>wheels</u> does work as it <u>slows down</u>. It causes an energy transfer from the <u>wheels' kinetic energy</u> stores to the <u>thermal</u> energy store of the <u>surroundings</u>.

frictional forces cause a transfer of energy

In a collision between a car and a <u>stationary object</u>, the <u>normal contact force</u> between the car and the object <u>does work</u>. It causes energy to be transferred from the car's <u>kinetic</u> energy store to <u>other energy stores</u>, e.g. the <u>elastic potential</u> and <u>thermal energy</u> stores of the object and the car body. Some energy might also be <u>transferred away</u> by <u>sound</u> waves (see p.88).

All this work, I can feel my energy stores being drained...

Energy stores pop up everywhere in physics, the pesky scoundrels — make sure you've got to grips with them.

Q1   Describe the energy transfers that occur when the wind causes a windmill to spin.   [3 marks]

Kinetic and Potential Energy Stores

Now you've got your head around <u>energy stores</u>, it's time to see how you can calculate the amount of energy in <u>three</u> of the most common ones — <u>kinetic</u>, <u>gravitational potential</u> and <u>elastic potential</u> energy stores.

Movement Means Energy in an Object's Kinetic Energy Store

1) Anything that is <u>moving</u> has energy in its <u>kinetic energy store</u>. Energy is transferred <u>to</u> this store when an object <u>speeds up</u> and is transferred <u>away</u> from this store when an object <u>slows down</u>.

2) The energy in the <u>kinetic energy store</u> depends on the object's <u>mass</u> and <u>speed</u>. The <u>greater its mass</u> and the <u>faster</u> it's going, the <u>more energy</u> there will be in its kinetic energy store.

3) There's a <u>slightly tricky</u> formula for it, so you have to concentrate <u>a little bit harder</u> for this one.

EXAMPLE:

A car of mass 2500 kg is travelling at 20 m/s. Calculate the energy in its kinetic energy store.

$E_k = \frac{1}{2} \times 2500 \times 20^2 = 500\ 000$ J

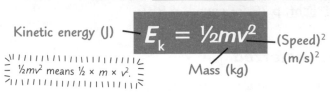

Kinetic energy (J)

$$E_k = \frac{1}{2}mv^2$$

(Speed)^2 (m/s)^2

½mv² means ½ × m × v².

Mass (kg)

Raised Objects Store Energy in Gravitational Potential Energy Stores

1) <u>Lifting</u> an object in a <u>gravitational field</u> requires <u>work</u>. This causes a <u>transfer of energy</u> to the <u>gravitational potential</u> energy (g.p.e.) store of the raised object. The <u>higher</u> the object is lifted, the <u>more</u> energy is transferred to this store.

2) The amount of energy in a g.p.e. store depends on the object's <u>mass</u>, its <u>height</u> and the <u>strength</u> of the gravitational field the object is in (p.52).

g.p.e (J)

$$E_p = mgh$$

Height (m)

Mass (kg)

Gravitational field strength (N/kg)

3) You can use this equation to find the <u>change in energy</u> in an object's gravitational potential energy store for a <u>change in height</u>, <u>h</u>.

Falling Objects Also Transfer Energy

1) When something <u>falls</u>, energy from its <u>gravitational potential energy store</u> is transferred to its <u>kinetic energy store</u>.

2) For a falling object when there's <u>no air resistance</u>:

> Energy lost from the g.p.e. store = Energy gained in the kinetic energy store

3) In real life, <u>air resistance</u> (p.63) acts against all falling objects — it causes some energy to be transferred to <u>other energy stores</u>, e.g. the <u>thermal</u> energy stores of the <u>object</u> and <u>surroundings</u>.

GPE
↓
KE

Stretching can Transfer Energy to Elastic Potential Energy Stores

<u>Stretching</u> or <u>squashing</u> an object can transfer energy to its <u>elastic potential energy store</u>. So long as the <u>limit of proportionality</u> has not been <u>exceeded</u> (p.55) energy in the <u>elastic potential energy store</u> of a stretched spring can be found using:

Spring constant (N/m)

Elastic potential energy (J)

$$E_e = \frac{1}{2}ke^2$$

Extension (m)

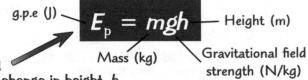

Make the most of your potential — jump on your bed...

Wow, that's a lot of energy equations. Make sure you know how to use them all, and remember that the energy in an object's kinetic energy store only changes if it's changing its speed. Now have a crack at this delightful question...

Q1 A 2.0 kg object is dropped from a height of 10 m. Calculate the speed of the object after it has fallen 5.0 m, assuming there is no air resistance. Give your answer to 2 significant figures. $g = 9.8$ N/kg. [5 marks]

Specific Heat Capacity

Specific heat capacity is really just a sciencey way of saying how hard it is to heat something up...

Different Materials Have Different Specific Heat Capacities

1) More energy needs to be transferred to the thermal energy store of some materials to increase their temperature than others. E.g. you need 4200 J to warm 1 kg of water by 1 °C, but only 139 J to warm 1 kg of mercury by 1 °C.

2) Materials that need to gain lots of energy in their thermal energy stores to warm up also transfer loads of energy when they cool down again. They can 'store' a lot of energy.

3) Specific heat capacity is the amount of energy needed to raise the temperature of 1 kg of a substance by 1 °C.

4) Here's the equation that links energy transferred to specific heat capacity: (the Δ's just mean "change in").

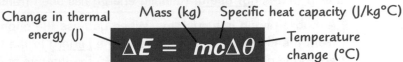

Change in thermal energy (J)   Mass (kg)   Specific heat capacity (J/kg°C)

$$\Delta E = mc\Delta\theta$$

Temperature change (°C)

You Can Investigate Specific Heat Capacities

PRACTICAL

1) To investigate a solid material (e.g. copper), you'll need a block of the material with two holes in it (for the heater and thermometer to go into, see below).

2) Measure the mass of the block, then wrap it in an insulating layer (e.g. a thick layer of newspaper) to reduce the energy transferred from the block to the surroundings. Insert the thermometer and heater as shown on the right.

3) Measure the initial temperature of the block and set the potential difference, V, of the power supply to be 10 V. Turn on the power supply and start a stop watch.

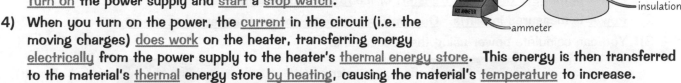

power supply   heater   thermometer   block of material   insulation   ammeter

4) When you turn on the power, the current in the circuit (i.e. the moving charges) does work on the heater, transferring energy electrically from the power supply to the heater's thermal energy store. This energy is then transferred to the material's thermal energy store by heating, causing the material's temperature to increase.

5) As the block heats up, take readings of the temperature and current, I, every minute for 10 minutes. You should find that the current through the circuit doesn't change as the block heats up.

6) When you've collected enough readings (10 should do it), turn off the power supply. Using your measurement of the current, and the potential difference of the power supply, you can calculate the power supplied to the heater, using $P = VI$ (p.33). You can use this to calculate how much energy, E, has been transferred to the heater at the time of each temperature reading using the formula $E = Pt$, where t is the time in seconds since the experiment began.

7) If you assume all the energy supplied to the heater has been transferred to the block, you can plot a graph of energy transferred to the thermal energy store of the block against temperature. It should look something like this: ⟹ (you may or may not get the curved bit at the beginning, don't worry about it).

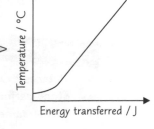

Temperature / °C

Energy transferred / J

8) Find the gradient of the straight part of the graph. This is $\Delta\theta \div \Delta E$. You know from the equation above that $\Delta E = mc\Delta\theta$. So the specific heat capacity of the material of the block is: $1 \div (\text{gradient} \times \text{the mass of the block})$.

9) You can repeat this experiment with different materials to see how their specific heat capacities compare.

> You can also investigate the specific heat capacity of liquids — just place the heater and thermometer in an insulated beaker filled with a known mass of the liquid.

I've eaten five sausages — I have a high specific meat capacity...

The specific heat capacity equation looks a bit tricky, but like all equations, it's easy to use when you know how.

Q1   Find the final temperature of 5 kg of water, at an initial temperature of 5 °C, after 50 kJ of energy has been transferred to it. The specific heat capacity of water is 4200 J/kg°C.   [3 marks]

Conservation of Energy and Power

Repeat after me: <u>energy</u> is <u>NEVER</u> destroyed. Make sure you learn that fact, it's really important.

You Need to Know the Conservation of Energy Principle

1) The <u>conservation of energy principle</u> is that energy is <u>always</u> conserved:

> Energy can be <u>transferred</u> usefully, stored or dissipated, but can <u>never</u> be <u>created</u> or <u>destroyed</u>.

2) When energy is <u>transferred</u> between stores, not <u>all</u> of the energy is transferred <u>usefully</u> into the store that you want it to go to. Some energy is always <u>dissipated</u> when an energy transfer takes place.

3) Dissipated energy is sometimes called '<u>wasted energy</u>' because the energy is being <u>stored</u> in a way that is <u>not useful</u> (usually energy has been transferred into thermal energy stores).

> A mobile phone is a <u>system</u>. When you use the phone, energy is <u>usefully</u> transferred from the <u>chemical</u> energy store of the <u>battery</u> in the phone. But some of this energy is <u>dissipated</u> in this transfer to the <u>thermal</u> energy store of the <u>phone</u> (you may have noticed your phone feels warm if you've been using it for a while).

4) You also need to be able to describe energy transfers for <u>closed systems</u>:

> A <u>cold spoon</u> is dropped into an insulated flask of <u>hot soup</u>, which is then sealed. You can assume that the flask is a <u>perfect thermal insulator</u> so the <u>spoon</u> and the <u>soup</u> form a <u>closed system</u>. Energy is transferred from the <u>thermal</u> energy store of the <u>soup</u> to the <u>useless</u> thermal energy store of the <u>spoon</u> (causing the soup to cool down slightly). Energy transfers have occurred <u>within</u> the system, but no energy has <u>left</u> the system — so the net change in energy is <u>zero</u>, p.11.

Power is the 'Rate of Doing Work' — i.e. How Much per Second

1) Power is the <u>rate of energy transfer</u>, or the <u>rate of doing work</u>.

2) <u>Power</u> is measured in <u>watts</u>. One watt = 1 joule of energy transferred per second.

3) You can calculate power using these equations:

$$P = \frac{E}{t}$$ Power (W) — Energy transferred (J) — Time (s)

$$P = \frac{W}{t}$$ Power (W) — Work done (J) — Time (s)

4) A <u>powerful</u> machine is not necessarily one which can exert a strong <u>force</u> (although it usually ends up that way). A <u>powerful</u> machine is one which transfers <u>a lot of energy</u> in a <u>short space of time</u>.

> Take two cars that are <u>identical</u> in every way apart from the <u>power</u> of their <u>engines</u>. Both cars race the <u>same distance</u> along a straight race track to a finish line. The car with the <u>more powerful</u> engine will reach the finish line <u>faster</u> than the other car — i.e. it will transfer the <u>same amount of energy</u> but over <u>less time</u>.
>

EXAMPLE:

It takes 8000 J of work to lift a stunt performer to the top of a building. Motor A can lift the stunt performer to the correct height in 50 s. Motor B would take 300 s to lift the performer to the same height. Which motor is most powerful? Calculate the power of this motor.

1) Both motors transfer the same amount of energy, but motor A would do it quicker than motor B. So, <u>motor A</u> is the more powerful motor.

2) Plug the time taken and work done for motor A into the equation $P = W \div t$ and find the power.
$P = W \div t = 8000 \div 50 = 160 \text{ W}$

Energy can't be created or destroyed — only talked about a lot...

Remember, when energy is wasted it's <u>not destroyed</u> — it still exists, it just isn't stored usefully anymore.

Q1   A motor transfers 4.8 kJ of energy in 2 minutes. Calculate its power output.   [3 marks]

Conduction and Convection

You __DON'T__ need to be able to explain the ins and outs of <u>conduction</u> and <u>convection</u>, but you need to know about them so you can understand energy transfers <u>by heating</u> (and how to reduce them — see next page).

Conduction Occurs Mainly in Solids

> __CONDUCTION__ is the process where <u>VIBRATING PARTICLES</u> <u>TRANSFER ENERGY</u> to <u>NEIGHBOURING PARTICLES</u>.

Particles in liquids and gases are much more free to move around, which is why they usually transfer energy by convection instead of conduction.

1) Energy transferred to an object <u>by heating</u> is transferred to the <u>thermal store</u> of the object. This energy is shared across the <u>kinetic</u> energy stores of the <u>particles</u> in the object.

2) The particles in the part of the object being heated <u>vibrate</u> more and <u>collide</u> with each other. These <u>collisions</u> cause energy to be transferred between particles' <u>kinetic</u> energy stores. This is <u>conduction</u>.

3) This process <u>continues throughout</u> the object until the energy is transferred to the <u>other side</u> of the object. It's then usually transferred to the <u>thermal</u> energy store of the <u>surroundings</u> (or anything else <u>touching</u> the object).

H O T   Energy transfer   C O L D

4) <u>Thermal conductivity</u> is a measure of how <u>quickly</u> energy is transferred through a material in this way. Materials with a <u>high thermal conductivity</u> transfer energy between their particles <u>quickly</u>.

Convection Occurs Only in Liquids and Gases

> __CONVECTION__ is where energetic particles <u>MOVE AWAY</u> from <u>HOTTER</u> to <u>COOLER REGIONS</u>.

1) <u>Convection</u> can happen in <u>gases</u> and <u>liquids</u>. Energy is transferred <u>by heating</u> to the <u>thermal store</u> of the liquid or gas. Again, this energy is shared across the <u>kinetic</u> energy stores of the gas or liquid's particles.

2) Unlike in solids, the particles in liquids and gases are <u>able to move</u>. When you heat a region of a gas or liquid, the particles <u>move faster</u> and the <u>space</u> between individual particles <u>increases</u>. This causes the <u>density</u> (p.38) of the <u>region</u> being heated to <u>decrease</u>.

3) Because liquids and gases can <u>flow</u>, the warmer and less dense region will <u>rise</u> above <u>denser</u>, <u>cooler</u> regions. If there is a <u>constant</u> heat source, a <u>convection current</u> can be created.

Radiators Create Convection Currents

1) Heating a room with a <u>radiator</u> relies on creating <u>convection currents</u> in the <u>air</u> of the room.

2) Energy is <u>transferred from</u> the <u>radiator</u> to the nearby <u>air particles</u> by <u>conduction</u> (the air particles collide with the radiator surface).

3) The air by the radiator becomes <u>warmer</u> and <u>less dense</u> (as the particles move <u>quicker</u>).

4) This <u>warm air rises</u> and is replaced by <u>cooler air</u>. The cooler air is then heated by the radiator.

5) At the same time, the previously heated air transfers energy to the surroundings (e.g. the walls and contents of the room). It <u>cools</u>, becomes <u>denser</u> and <u>sinks</u>.

6) This cycle <u>repeats</u>, causing a <u>flow of air</u> to circulate around the room — this is a <u>convection current</u>.

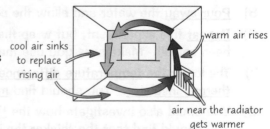
cool air sinks to replace rising air   warm air rises   air near the radiator gets warmer

I'd rather move away to a hotter region — Barbados maybe...

This might all sound like a load of particles now, but this stuff is really useful, especially when explaining how to stop unwanted transfers — there's more coming up on that in a tick.

Q1   Describe how energy is transferred through a solid by heating. What is the name of this effect? [3 marks]

Reducing Unwanted Energy Transfers

There are a few ways you can __reduce__ the amount of energy scampering off to a __completely useless__ store — __lubrication__ and __thermal insulation__ are the ones you need to know about. Read on...

Lubrication Reduces Frictional Forces

1) Whenever something __moves__, there's usually at least one __frictional force__ acting against it (p.63). This causes some energy in the system to be __dissipated__ (p.14), e.g. __air resistance__ can transfer energy from a falling object's __kinetic energy store__ to its __thermal energy store__.

2) For objects that are being rubbed together, __lubricants__ can be used to reduce the friction between the objects' surfaces when they move. Lubricants are usually __liquids__ (like __oil__), so they can __flow__ easily between objects and __coat__ them.

Streamlining reduces air resistance too, see p.63.

Insulation Reduces the Rate of Energy Transfer by Heating

The last thing you want when you've made your house nice and toasty is for that energy to __escape__ outside. There are a few things you can do to __prevent energy losses__ through __heating__:

• Have __thick walls__ that are made from a material with a __low thermal conductivity__. The __thicker__ the walls and the __lower__ their __thermal conductivity__, the __slower__ the rate of energy transfer will be (so the building will __cool more slowly__).

• Use __thermal insulation__. Here are some examples:

Reducing the difference between the temperature inside and outside the house will also reduce the rate of energy transfer.

1) Some houses have __cavity walls__, made up of an __inner__ and an __outer__ wall with an air gap in the middle. The __air gap__ reduces the amount of energy transferred by conduction through the walls. __Cavity wall insulation__, where the cavity wall air gap is filled with a __foam__, can also reduce energy transfer by __convection__ in the wall cavity.

2) __Loft insulation__ can reduce __convection__ currents being created in lofts.

3) __Double-glazed windows__ work in the same way as cavity walls — they have an air gap between two sheets of glass to prevent energy transfer by __conduction__ through the windows.

4) __Draught excluders__ around doors and windows reduce energy transfers by __convection__.

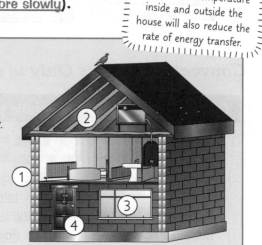

You Can Investigate the Effectiveness of Materials as Thermal Insulators

1) __Boil water__ in a kettle. Pour some of the water into a __sealable container__ (e.g. a beaker and lid) to a __safe level__. __Measure__ the mass of water in the container (p.104).

2) Use a __thermometer__ to measure the __initial temperature__ of the water.

3) __Seal__ the container and leave it for __five minutes__. Measure this time using a __stopwatch__.

4) Remove the lid and measure the __final temperature__ of the water.

5) __Pour away__ the water and allow the container to __cool__ to __room temperature__.

6) __Repeat__ this experiment, but wrap the container in a __different material__ (e.g. foil, newspaper) once it has been sealed. Make sure you use the __same mass__ of water at the same __initial temperature__ each time.

7) The lower the __temperature difference__ (and so __energy transferred__, p.13) the __better__ that material is as a __thermal insulator__. You should find __materials__ like __bubble wrap__ or __cotton wool__ are good thermal insulators.

8) You could also investigate how the __thickness__ of the material affects how good a __thermal insulator__ it is. You should find that the __thicker__ the insulating layer, the __smaller__ the __temperature change__ of the water, and so the __less__ energy is transferred. This means __thicker layers__ make __better__ thermal insulators.

PRACTICAL

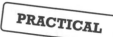

Bundle your brew in newspaper to stop it going cold...

Have a go at naming as many methods for reducing energy transfers as you can, then try this question.

Q1   Explain how cavity wall insulation reduces the amount of energy transferred out of a house. [3 marks]

Efficiency

More! More! Tell me more about <u>energy transfers</u> please! Oh go on then, since you insist...

Most Energy Transfers Involve Some Waste Energy

1) <u>Useful devices</u> are only <u>useful</u> because they can <u>transfer energy</u> from one store to another.

2) As you'll probably have gathered by now, some of the <u>input energy</u> is usually wasted by being transferred to a useless energy store — usually a <u>thermal energy store</u>.

3) The <u>less energy</u> that is 'wasted' in this energy store, the <u>more efficient</u> the device is said to be.

4) You can <u>improve</u> the efficiency of energy transfers by <u>insulating</u> objects, <u>lubricating</u> them or making them more <u>streamlined</u> (see pages 16 and 63).

5) The efficiency for any energy transfer can be <u>worked out</u> using this equation:

$$\text{Efficiency} = \frac{\text{Useful output energy transfer}}{\text{Total input energy transfer}}$$

You can give efficiency as a <u>decimal</u> or you can <u>multiply</u> your answer by 100 to get a <u>percentage</u>, i.e. <u>0.75</u> or <u>75%</u>.

6) You might not know the <u>energy</u> inputs and outputs of a device, but you can still calculate its efficiency as long as you know the <u>power input</u> and <u>output</u>:

$$\text{Efficiency} = \frac{\text{Useful power output}}{\text{Total power input}}$$

EXAMPLE: A blender is 70% efficient. It has a total input power of 600 W. Calculate the useful output power.

1) Change the <u>efficiency</u> from a <u>percentage</u> to a <u>decimal</u>.

2) <u>Rearrange</u> the equation for <u>useful power output</u>.

3) <u>Stick in</u> the numbers you're given.

efficiency = 70% = 0.7
useful power output = efficiency × total power input
= 0.7 × 600
= 420 W

Useful Energy Input Isn't Usually Equal to Total Energy Output

1) For any given example you can talk about the types of energy being input and output, but remember: <u>NO</u> device is <u>100% efficient</u> and the wasted energy is usually transferred to useless <u>thermal energy stores</u>.

2) <u>Electric heaters</u> are the <u>exception</u> to this. They're usually <u>100% efficient</u> because <u>all</u> the energy in the electrostatic energy store is transferred to "useful" thermal energy stores.

3) Ultimately, <u>all</u> energy ends up transferred to <u>thermal energy stores</u>. For example, if you use an <u>electric drill</u>, its energy transfers to lots of different energy stores, but quickly ends up all in thermal energy stores.

Don't waste your energy — turn the TV off while you revise...

Make sure you can use and rearrange the equations for efficiency, then have a go at these questions.

Q1 A motor in a remote-controlled car transfers 300 J of energy into the car's energy stores. 225 J are transferred to the car's kinetic energy stores. Calculate the efficiency of the motor. [2 marks]

Q2 A machine has a useful power output of 900 W and a total power input of 1200 W. In a given time, 72 kJ of energy is transferred to the machine. Calculate the amount of energy usefully transferred by the machine in this time. [4 marks]

Energy Resources and their Uses

Energy resources, both <u>renewable</u> and <u>non-renewable</u>, are mostly used to <u>generate electricity</u>.
There's loads more on how over the next few pages, but two other major uses are <u>transport</u> and <u>heating</u>.

Non-Renewable Energy Resources Will Run Out One Day

<u>Non-renewable</u> energy resources are <u>fossil fuels</u> and <u>nuclear fuel</u> (uranium and plutonium). <u>Fossil fuels</u> are natural resources that form <u>underground</u> over <u>millions</u> of years. They are typically <u>burnt</u> to provide energy. The <u>three main</u> fossil fuels are:

1) Coal
2) Oil
3) (Natural) Gas

- These will <u>all</u> 'run out' one day.
- They all do <u>damage</u> to the environment.
- But they provide <u>most of our energy</u>.

Renewable Energy Resources Will Never Run Out

<u>Renewable</u> energy resources are:

1) The Sun (Solar)
2) Wind
3) Water waves
4) Hydro-electricity
5) Bio-fuel
6) Tides
7) Geothermal

- These will <u>never run out</u> — the energy can be '<u>renewed</u>' as it is used.
- Most of them do <u>damage</u> the environment, but in <u>less nasty</u> ways than non-renewables.
- The trouble is they <u>don't</u> provide much <u>energy</u> and some of them are <u>unreliable</u> because they depend on the weather.

Energy Resources can be Used for Transport...

<u>Transport</u> is one of the most obvious places where <u>fuel</u> is used. Here are a few transportation methods that use either <u>renewable</u> or <u>non-renewable</u> energy resources:

Electricity can also be used to power vehicles, (e.g. trains and some cars). It can be generated using renewable or non-renewable energy resources (p.19-21).

NON-RENEWABLE ENERGY RESOURCES
- <u>Petrol</u> and <u>diesel</u> powered vehicles (including most cars) use fuel created from <u>oil</u>.
- <u>Coal</u> is used in some old-fashioned <u>steam trains</u> to boil water to produce steam.

RENEWABLE ENERGY RESOURCES
Vehicles that run on pure <u>bio-fuels</u> (p.21) or a <u>mix</u> of a bio-fuel and petrol or diesel (only the bio-fuel bit is renewable, though).

...And for Heating

<u>Energy resources</u> are also needed for <u>heating</u> things like your home.

NON-RENEWABLE ENERGY RESOURCES
- <u>Natural gas</u> is the most widely used fuel for heating homes in the UK. The gas is used to heat <u>water</u>, which is then pumped into <u>radiators</u> throughout the home.
  - <u>Coal</u> is commonly burnt in fireplaces.
  - <u>Electric heaters</u> (sometimes called storage heaters) which use electricity generated from <u>non-renewable</u> energy resources.

RENEWABLE ENERGY RESOURCES
- A <u>geothermal</u> (or ground source) <u>heat pump</u> uses geothermal energy resources (p.19) to heat buildings.
- <u>Solar water heaters</u> work by using the sun to heat <u>water</u> which is then pumped into radiators in the building.
- Burning <u>bio-fuel</u> or using <u>electricity</u> generated from renewable resources can also be used for heating.

I'm pretty sure natural gas is renewable — I make enough of it...

You need to know the difference between the two different types of energy resource, so get cracking.

Q1 Write down whether each of the following are renewable or non-renewable energy resources.
a) Tidal power   b) Natural gas   c) Nuclear power   d) Bio-fuel   [4 marks]

Wind, Solar and Geothermal

Renewable energy resources, like wind, solar and geothermal resources, will not run out. They don't generate as much electricity as non-renewables though — if they did we'd all be using solar-powered toasters by now.

Wind Power — Lots of Little Wind Turbines

1) This involves putting lots of wind turbines up in exposed places like on moors or round coasts.

2) Each turbine has a generator inside it — the rotating blades turn the generator and produce electricity (p.96).

3) There's no pollution (except for a little bit when they're manufactured).

4) But they do spoil the view. You need about 1500 wind turbines to replace one coal-fired power station and 1500 of them cover a lot of ground — which would have a big effect on the scenery.

5) And they can be very noisy, which can be annoying for people living nearby.

6) There's also the problem of the turbines stopping when the wind stops or if the wind is too strong, and it's impossible to increase supply when there's extra demand. On average, wind turbines produce electricity 70-85% of the time.

7) The initial costs are quite high, but there are no fuel costs and minimal running costs.

8) There's no permanent damage to the landscape — if you remove the turbines, you remove the noise and the view returns to normal.

Solar Cells — Expensive but No Environmental Damage

(well, there may be a bit caused by making the cells)

1) Solar cells generate electric currents directly from sunlight. Solar cells are often the best source of energy to charge batteries in calculators and watches which don't use much electricity.

2) Solar power is often used in remote places where there's not much choice (e.g. the Australian outback) and to power electric road signs and satellites.

3) There's no pollution. (Although they do use quite a lot of energy to manufacture in the first place.)

4) In sunny countries solar power is a very reliable source of energy — but only in the daytime. Solar power can still be cost-effective even in cloudy countries like Britain though.

5) Like wind, you can't increase the power output when there is extra demand (p.34).

6) Initial costs are high but after that the energy is free and running costs almost nil.

7) Solar cells are usually used to generate electricity on a relatively small scale.

Time to recharge.

Geothermal Power — Energy in Underground Thermal Energy Stores

1) This is possible in volcanic areas or where hot rocks lie quite near to the surface. The source of much of the energy is the slow decay of various radioactive elements, including uranium, deep inside the Earth.

2) This is actually brilliant free energy that's reliable and does very little damage to the environment.

3) Geothermal power can be used to generate electricity, or to heat buildings directly.

4) The main drawbacks with geothermal power are that there aren't very many suitable locations for power plants, and that the cost of building a power plant is often high compared to the amount of energy it produces.

People love the idea of wind power — just not in their back yard...

There are pros and cons to all energy resources. Make sure you know them for solar, wind and geothermal.

Q1   Explain why geothermal power is more reliable than wind power.   [2 marks]

Hydro-electricity, Waves and Tides

Good ol' water. Not only can we drink it, we can also use it to generate electricity. It's easy to get confused between wave and tidal power as they both involve the seaside — but don't. They are completely different.

Hydro-electric Power Uses Falling Water

1) Hydro-electric power usually requires the flooding of a valley by building a big dam. Water is allowed out through turbines. There is no pollution (as such).

2) But there is a big impact on the environment due to the flooding of the valley (rotting vegetation releases methane and CO_2) and possible loss of habitat for some species (sometimes the loss of whole villages). The reservoirs can also look very unsightly when they dry up. Putting hydroelectric power stations in remote valleys tends to reduce their impact on humans.

3) A big advantage is it can provide an immediate response to an increased demand for electricity.

4) There's no problem with reliability except in times of drought — but remember this is Great Britain we're talking about.

5) Initial costs are high, but there are no fuel costs and minimal running costs.

6) It can be a useful way to generate electricity on a small scale in remote areas.

Wave Power — Lots of Little Wave-Powered Turbines

1) You need lots of small wave-powered turbines located around the coast. Like with wind power (p.19) the moving turbines are connected to a generator.

2) There is no pollution. The main problems are disturbing the seabed and the habitats of marine animals, spoiling the view and being a hazard to boats.

3) They are fairly unreliable, since waves tend to die out when the wind drops.

4) Initial costs are high, but there are no fuel costs and minimal running costs. Wave power is never likely to provide energy on a large scale, but it can be very useful on small islands.

Tidal Barrages — Using the Sun and Moon's Gravity

1) Tides are used in lots of ways to generate electricity. The most common method is building a tidal barrage.

2) Tidal barrages are big dams built across river estuaries, with turbines in them. As the tide comes in it fills up the estuary. The water is then allowed out through turbines at a controlled speed.

3) Tides are produced by the gravitational pull of the Sun and Moon.

4) There is no pollution. The main problems are preventing free access by boats, spoiling the view and altering the habitat of the wildlife, e.g. wading birds, sea creatures and beasties who live in the sand.

5) Tides are pretty reliable in the sense that they happen twice a day without fail, and always near to the predicted height. The only drawback is that the height of the tide is variable so lower (neap) tides will provide significantly less energy than the bigger 'spring' tides. They also don't work when the water level is the same either side of the barrage — this happens four times a day because of the tides.

6) Initial costs are moderately high, but there are no fuel costs and minimal running costs. Even though it can only be used in some of the most suitable estuaries tidal power has the potential for generating a significant amount of energy.

The hydro-electric power you're supplying — it's electrifying...

Learn the differences between all of these water-based resources before having a go at this question.

Q1   Give one negative environmental impact of wave power.   [1 mark]

Bio-fuels and Non-renewables

And the energy resources just keep on coming. It's over soon, I promise. Just a few more to go.

Bio-fuels are Made from Plants and Waste

1) Bio-fuels are renewable energy resources created from either plant products or animal dung. They can be solid, liquid or gas and can be burnt to produce electricity or run cars in the same way as fossil fuels.

2) They are supposedly carbon neutral, although there is some debate about this as it's only really true if you keep growing plants at the rate that you're burning things.

3) Bio-fuels are fairly reliable, as crops take a relatively short time to grow and different crops can be grown all year round. However, they cannot respond to immediate energy demands. To combat this, bio-fuels are continuously produced and stored for when they are needed.

4) The cost to refine bio-fuels is very high and some worry that growing crops specifically for bio-fuels will mean there isn't enough space or water to meet the demands for crops that are grown for food.

5) In some regions, large areas of forest have been cleared to make room to grow bio-fuels, resulting in lots of species losing their natural habitats. The decay and burning of this vegetation also increases CO_2 and methane emissions.

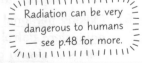

Non-Renewables are Reliable...

1) Fossil fuels and nuclear energy are reliable. There's enough fossil and nuclear fuels to meet current demand, and they are extracted from the Earth at a fast enough rate that power plants always have fuel in stock. This means that the power plants can respond quickly to changes in demand (p.34).

Nuclear power plants use fission to produce electricity (p.49).

2) However, these fuels are slowly running out. If no new resources are found, some fossil fuel stocks may run out within a hundred years.

3) While the set-up costs of power plants can be quite high compared to some other energy resources, the running costs aren't that expensive. Combined with fairly low fuel extraction costs, using fossil fuels is a cost effective way to produce energy (which is why it's so popular).

...But Create Environmental Problems

1) Coal, oil and gas release CO_2 into the atmosphere when they're burned. All this CO_2 adds to the greenhouse effect, and contributes to global warming.

2) Burning coal and oil also releases sulfur dioxide, which causes acid rain — which can be harmful to trees and soils and can have far-reaching effects in ecosystems.

3) Acid rain can be reduced by taking the sulfur out before the fuel is burned, or cleaning up the emissions.

4) Coal mining makes a mess of the landscape, especially "open-cast mining". As with many energy resources, the view can be spoilt by fossil fuel power plants.

5) Oil spillages cause serious environmental problems, affecting mammals and birds that live in and around the sea. We try to avoid them, but they'll always happen.

6) Nuclear power is clean but the nuclear waste is very dangerous and difficult to dispose of.

7) Nuclear fuel (e.g. uranium or plutonium) is relatively cheap but the overall cost of nuclear power is high due to the cost of the power plant and final decommissioning.

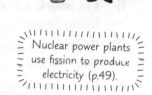

Radiation can be very dangerous to humans — see p.48 for more.

8) Nuclear power always carries the risk of a major catastrophe like the Fukushima disaster in Japan.

Bio-fuels are great — but don't burn your biology notes just yet...

Make sure you can talk about the reliability and any environmental issues of using bio-fuels or non-renewables.

Q1   Give two benefits of power plants that use fossil fuels.   [2 marks]

Q2   Describe the environmental impact of using oil as an energy resource for generating electricity.   [3 marks]

Trends in Energy Resource Use

Over time, the types of energy resources we use change. There are lots of reasons for this — breakthroughs in technology, understanding more about how they affect the environment or changes in cost are just a few.

Currently we Still Depend on Fossil Fuels

See p.34 for more about the supply and demand of electricity.

1) Over the 20th century, the electricity use of the UK hugely increased as the population grew and people began to use electricity for more and more things.

2) Since the beginning of the 21st century, electricity use in the UK has been decreasing (slowly), as we get better at making appliances more efficient (p.17) and become more careful with energy use in our homes.

3) Most of our electricity is produced using fossil fuels (mostly coal and gas) and from nuclear power.

4) Generating electricity isn't the only reason we burn fossil fuels — oil (diesel and petrol) is used to fuel cars, and gas is used to heat homes and cook food.

5) However, we are trying to increase our use of renewable energy resources (the UK aims to use renewable resources to provide 15% of its total yearly energy by 2020). This move towards renewable energy resources has been triggered by many things...

People Want to use More Renewable Energy Resources

1) We now know that burning fossil fuels is very damaging to the environment (p.21). This makes many people want to use more renewable energy resources that effect the environment less.

2) People and governments are also becoming increasingly aware that non-renewables will run out one day. Many people think it's better to learn to get by without non-renewables before this happens.

3) Pressure from other countries and the public has meant that governments have begun to introduce targets for using renewable resources. This in turn puts pressure on energy providers to build new power plants that use renewable resources to make sure they do not lose business and money.

4) Car companies have also been affected by this change in attitude towards the environment. Electric cars and hybrids (cars powered by two fuels, e.g. petrol and electricity) are already on the market and their popularity is increasing.

The Use of Renewables is Limited by Reliability, Money and Politics

1) There's a lot of scientific evidence supporting renewables, but although scientists can give advice, they don't have the power to make people, companies or governments change their behaviour (see p.2).

2) Building new renewable power plants costs money, so some energy providers are reluctant to do this, especially when fossil fuels are so cost effective. The cost of switching to renewable power will have to be paid, either by customers in their bills, or through government and taxes. Some people don't want to or can't afford to pay, and there are arguments about whether it's ethical to make them.

3) Even if new power plants are built, there are arguments over where to put them. E.g. many people don't want to live next to a wind farm, causing protests. There are arguments over whether it's ethical to make people put up with wind farms built next to them when they may not agree with the reasons for their use.

4) Some energy resources like wind power are not as reliable as traditional fossil fuels, whilst others cannot increase their power output on demand. This would mean either having to use a combination of different power plants (which would be expensive) or researching ways to improve reliability.

5) Research on improving the reliability and cost of renewables takes time and money — it may be years before improvements are made even with funding. Until then, we need dependable, non-renewable power.

6) Making personal changes can also be quite expensive. Hybrid cars are generally more expensive than equivalent petrol cars and things like solar panels for your home are still quite pricey. The cost of these things is slowly going down, but they are still not an option for many people.

Going green is on-trend this season...

So with more people wanting to help the environment, others not wanting to be inconvenienced and greener alternatives being expensive to set up, the energy resources we use are changing. Just not particularly quickly.

Q1   Give two reasons we currently do not use more renewable energy resources in the UK.   [2 marks]

Revision Questions for Topic 1

Well, that wraps up <u>Topic 1</u> — time to put yourself to the test and find out <u>how much you really know</u>.
- Try these questions and <u>tick off each one</u> when you <u>get it right</u>.
- When you've done <u>all the questions</u> for a subtopic and are <u>completely happy</u> with it, tick off the subtopic.

Energy Stores and Systems (p.11-12) ☑

1) Write down four energy stores. ☑
2) Describe how energy is transferred as a ball falls to the ground. ☑
3) Give the equation for calculating the amount of energy in an object's kinetic energy store. ☑
4) If energy is transferred to an object's kinetic energy store, what happens to its speed? ☑
5) Give the equation for finding the energy in an object's gravitational potential energy store. ☑
6) What kind of energy store is energy transferred to when you compress a spring? ☑

Specific Heat Capacity (p.13) ☑

7) What is the definition of the specific heat capacity of a material? ☑
8) Give the equation that relates energy transferred and specific heat capacity. ☑
9) Describe an experiment to find the specific heat capacity of a material. ☑

Conservation of Energy and Power (p.14) ☑

10) State the conservation of energy principle. ☑
11) Define power and give two equations to calculate power. ☑
12) What are the units of power? ☑

Reducing Unwanted Energy Transfers and Improving Efficiency (p.15-17) ☑

13) True or false? A high thermal conductivity means there is a high rate of energy transfer. ☑
14) How can you reduce unwanted energy transfers in a machine with moving, touching components? ☑
15) Give four ways to prevent unwanted energy transfers in a home. ☑
16) True or false? Thicker walls make a house cool down quicker. ☑
17) Describe an experiment you could do to investigate how good a material is as a thermal insulator. ☑
18) What is the efficiency of an energy transfer? Give the equation that relates efficiency to power. ☑

Energy Resources and Trends in their Use (p.18-22) ☑

19) Name four renewable energy resources and four non-renewable energy resources. ☑
20) What is the difference between renewable and non-renewable energy resources? ☑
21) Give an example of how a renewable energy resource is used in everyday life. ☑
22) Explain why solar power is considered to be a fairly reliable energy resource. ☑
23) True or false? Tidal barrages are useful for storing energy to be used during times of high demand. ☑
24) Describe one way of reducing the environmental impact of using fossil fuels. ☑
25) Give one environmental benefit of using nuclear power. ☑
26) Explain why the UK plans to use more renewable energy resources in the future. ☑

Current and Circuit Symbols

It's pretty bad news if the word <u>current</u> makes you think of delicious cakes instead of physics. Learn what it means, as well as some handy <u>symbols</u> to show items like <u>batteries</u> and <u>switches</u> in a circuit.

Current is the Flow of Electrical Charge

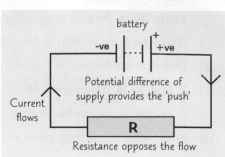

1) <u>Electric current</u> is a flow of <u>electrical charge</u>. Electrical charge will <u>only flow</u> round a complete (closed) circuit if there is a <u>potential difference</u>, so a current can only flow if there's a source of potential difference. The unit of current is the <u>ampere</u>, A.

2) In a <u>single</u>, closed <u>loop</u> (like the one on the right) the current has the same value <u>everywhere</u> in the circuit (see p.28).

3) <u>Potential difference</u> (or voltage) is the <u>driving force</u> that <u>pushes</u> the charge round. Its unit is the <u>volt</u>, V.

4) <u>Resistance</u> is anything that <u>slows the flow</u> down. Unit: <u>ohm</u>, Ω.

5) The current flowing <u>through a component</u> depends on the <u>potential difference</u> across it and the <u>resistance</u> of the component (p.25).

> The <u>greater the resistance</u> across a component, the <u>smaller the current</u> that flows (for a <u>given potential difference</u> across the component).

Total Charge Through a Circuit Depends on Current and Time

The size of the <u>current</u> is the <u>rate of flow</u> of <u>charge</u>. When <u>current</u> flows past a point in a circuit for a length of <u>time</u> then the <u>charge</u> that has passed is given by this formula:

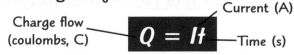

Charge flow (coulombs, C) — $Q = It$ — Current (A) — Time (s)

<u>More charge</u> passes around the circuit when a <u>larger current</u> flows.

EXAMPLE:

A battery charger passes a current of 2.0 A through a cell over a period of 2.5 hours. How much charge is transferred to the cell?

$Q = It = 2.0 \times (2.5 \times 60 \times 60)$
$\quad\quad = 18\ 000\ C$

Learn these Circuit Diagram Symbols

You need to be able to <u>understand circuit diagrams</u> and draw them using the <u>correct symbols</u>. Make sure all the <u>wires</u> in your circuit are <u>straight lines</u> and that the circuit is <u>closed</u>, i.e. you can follow a wire from one end of the power supply, through any components, to the other end of the supply (ignoring any <u>switches</u>).

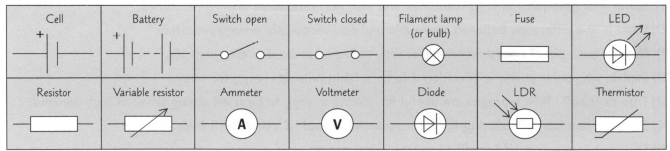

Cell	Battery	Switch open	Switch closed	Filament lamp (or bulb)	Fuse	LED
Resistor	Variable resistor	Ammeter	Voltmeter	Diode	LDR	Thermistor

---

I think it's about time you took charge...

You've no doubt seen some of those circuit symbols before, but take a good look at all of them and practise drawing them. It's no good if you get asked to draw a circuit diagram and you can't tell a resistor from a fuse.

Q1   A laptop charger passes a current of 8.0 A through a laptop battery. Calculate how long the charger needs to be connected to the battery for 28 800 C of charge to be transferred to the laptop.   [3 marks]

Q2   A student creates a simple circuit containing a battery, a switch and a bulb. He connects them all in a single, closed loop. Draw the circuit diagram for this circuit.   [3 marks]

Resistance and V = IR

Ooh experiments, you've gotta love 'em. Here's a <u>simple experiment</u> for investigating resistance.

There's a Formula Linking Potential Difference and Current

The formula linking pd and current is very useful (and pretty common):

> **Potential difference (V) = Current (A) × Resistance (Ω)**

Use this formula triangle to rearrange. Just cover up the thing you're trying to find, and what's left visible is the formula you're after.

EXAMPLE: A 4.0 Ω resistor in a circuit has a potential difference of 6.0 V across it. What is the current through the resistor?

<u>Rearrange</u> $V = IR$ to give $I = V \div R$, then <u>substitute</u> in the values you have. $I = 6.0 \div 4.0 = 1.5$ A

You Can Investigate the Factors Affecting Resistance

> PRACTICAL

The <u>resistance</u> of a circuit can depend on a number of factors, like whether components are in <u>series</u> or <u>parallel</u>, p.31, or the <u>length of wire</u> used in the circuit. You can investigate the effect of <u>wire length</u> using the circuit below.

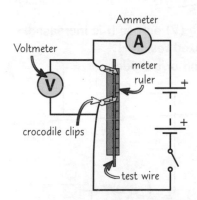

The Ammeter

1) Measures the <u>current</u> (in <u>amps</u>) flowing through the test wire.
2) The ammeter must always be placed <u>in series</u> with whatever you're investigating.

See p.28-29 for more on series and parallel circuits.

The Voltmeter

1) Measures the <u>potential difference</u> (or pd) across the test wire (in <u>volts</u>).
2) The voltmeter must always be placed <u>in parallel</u> around whatever you're investigating (p.29) — <u>**NOT**</u> around any other bit of the circuit, e.g. the battery.

A thin wire will give you the best results. Make sure it's as straight as possible so your length measurements are accurate.

1) Attach a <u>crocodile clip</u> to the wire level with <u>0 cm</u> on the ruler.
2) Attach the <u>second crocodile clip</u> to the wire, e.g. 10 cm away from the first clip. Write down the <u>length</u> of the wire between the clips.
3) <u>Close the switch</u>, then record the <u>current</u> through the wire and the <u>pd</u> across it.
4) <u>Open the switch</u>, then move the second crocodile clip, e.g. another 10 cm, along the wire. Close the switch again, then record the <u>new length</u>, <u>current</u> and <u>pd</u>.
5) <u>Repeat</u> this for a number of different lengths of the test wire.
6) Use your measurements of current and pd to <u>calculate</u> the <u>resistance</u> for each length of wire, using $R = V \div I$ (from $V = IR$).
7) Plot a <u>graph</u> of <u>resistance</u> against <u>wire length</u> and draw a <u>line of best fit</u>.
8) Your graph should be a <u>straight line</u> through the <u>origin</u>, meaning resistance is <u>directly proportional</u> to length — the <u>longer</u> the wire, the <u>greater</u> the resistance.
9) If your graph <u>doesn't</u> go through the origin, it could be because the <u>first clip</u> isn't attached exactly at 0 cm, so all of your length readings are a <u>bit out</u>. This is a <u>systematic error</u> (p.5).

The wire may heat up during the experiment, which will affect its resistance (p.26). Leave the switch open for a bit between readings to let the circuit cool down.

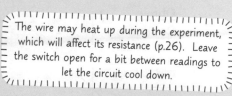

Measure gymnastics — use a vaultmeter...

You could also investigate the effect of diameter or material on the resistance of a wire. What fun.

Q1   An appliance is connected to a 230 V source. Calculate the resistance of the appliance if a current of 5.0 A is flowing through it.

[3 marks]

Resistance and I-V Characteristics

Time to investigate just how <u>current</u> varies with <u>potential difference</u>. Then you can make some <u>sweet graphs</u>...

Ohmic Conductors Have a Constant Resistance

For some components, as the <u>current</u> through them is changed,
the <u>resistance</u> of the component changes as well.

1) The <u>resistance</u> of <u>ohmic conductors</u> (e.g. a <u>wire</u> or a <u>resistor</u>) doesn't
change with the <u>current</u>. At a <u>constant temperature</u>, the current flowing through an ohmic conductor
is <u>directly proportional</u> to the potential difference across it. (R is constant in $V = IR$, previous page.)

2) The resistance of <u>some</u> resistors and components <u>DOES</u> change, e.g. a <u>diode</u> or a <u>filament lamp</u>.

3) When an <u>electrical charge</u> flows through a filament lamp, it <u>transfers</u> some energy to the
<u>thermal energy store</u> (p.11) of the filament, which is designed to <u>heat up</u>. <u>Resistance</u> increases with
<u>temperature</u>, so as the <u>current</u> increases, the filament lamp heats up more and the resistance increases.

4) For <u>diodes</u>, the resistance depends on the <u>direction</u> of the current. They will happily let
current flow in one direction, but have a <u>very high resistance</u> if it is <u>reversed</u>.

Three Very Important I-V Characteristics | PRACTICAL |

The term '<u>I-V characteristic</u>' refers to a <u>graph</u> which shows how the
<u>current</u> (<u>I</u>) flowing through a component changes as the <u>potential difference</u> (<u>V</u>) across it is increased.
<u>Linear</u> components have an <u>I-V</u> characteristic that's a <u>straight line</u> (e.g. a fixed resistor).
<u>Non-linear</u> components have a <u>curved</u> <u>I-V</u> characteristic (e.g. a filament lamp or a diode).

This type of circuit uses direct current (dc) (p.31) and is a series circuit (p.28).

You can do this <u>experiment</u> to find a component's <u>I-V</u> characteristic:

1) Set up the <u>test circuit</u> shown on the right.

2) Begin to vary the variable resistor. This alters the <u>current</u> flowing
through the circuit and the <u>potential difference</u> across the <u>component</u>.

3) Take several <u>pairs of readings</u> from the <u>ammeter</u> and <u>voltmeter</u>
to see how the <u>potential difference</u> across the component <u>varies</u>
as the <u>current changes</u>. Repeat each reading twice more to get
an <u>average</u> pd at each current.

4) <u>Swap</u> over the wires connected to the cell, so the <u>direction of the current</u> is reversed.

5) <u>Plot a graph</u> of <u>current against voltage</u> for the component.

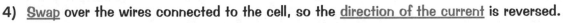

6) The <u>I-V</u> characteristics you get for an <u>ohmic conductor</u>, <u>filament lamp</u> and <u>diode</u> should look like this:

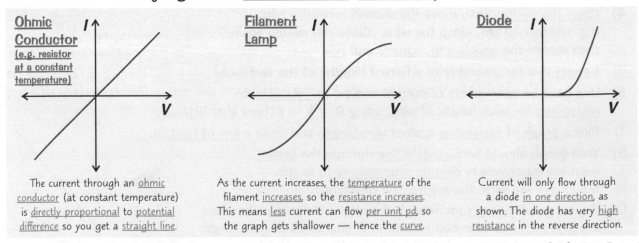

Ohmic Conductor (e.g. resistor at a constant temperature)

The current through an <u>ohmic conductor</u> (at constant temperature) is <u>directly proportional</u> to <u>potential difference</u> so you get a <u>straight line</u>.

Filament Lamp

As the current increases, the <u>temperature</u> of the filament <u>increases</u>, so the <u>resistance increases</u>. This means <u>less</u> current can flow <u>per unit pd</u>, so the graph gets shallower — hence the <u>curve</u>.

Diode

Current will only flow through a diode <u>in one direction</u>, as shown. The diode has very <u>high resistance</u> in the reverse direction.

Since $V = IR$, you can calculate the <u>resistance</u> at any <u>point</u> on the <u>I-V</u> characteristic by calculating $R = V/I$.

In the end you'll have to learn this — resistance is futile...

Draw out those graphs until you're sketching them in your sleep and make sure you can tell whether they're
showing a linear or non-linear component.

Q1   Draw the *I-V* characteristic for: a) an ohmic conductor   b) a filament lamp   [4 marks]

Circuit Devices

The fun doesn't stop with <u>filament bulbs</u>. As well as <u>temperature</u>, <u>resistance</u> can depend on things like <u>light intensity</u>, which is how <u>LDRs</u> work. They're really useful for circuits that sense changes in <u>light levels</u>.

LDR is Short for Light Dependent Resistor

1) An LDR is a resistor that is <u>dependent</u> on the <u>intensity</u> of <u>light</u>. Simple really.
2) In <u>bright light</u>, the resistance <u>falls</u>.
3) In <u>darkness</u>, the resistance is <u>highest</u>.
4) They have lots of applications including <u>automatic night lights</u>, outdoor lighting and <u>burglar detectors</u>.

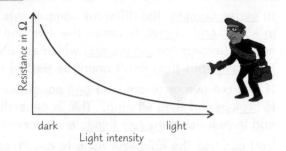

The Resistance of a Thermistor Depends on Temperature

1) A <u>thermistor</u> is a <u>temperature dependent</u> resistor.
2) In <u>hot</u> conditions, the resistance <u>drops</u>.
3) In <u>cool</u> conditions, the resistance goes <u>up</u>.
4) Thermistors make useful <u>temperature detectors</u>, e.g. <u>car engine</u> temperature sensors and electronic <u>thermostats</u>.

You Can Use LDRs and Thermistors in Sensing Circuits

1) <u>Sensing circuits</u> can be used to <u>turn on</u> or <u>increase the power</u> to components depending on the <u>conditions</u> that they are in.
2) The circuit on the right is a <u>sensing circuit</u> used to control a fan in a room.
3) The fixed resistor and the fan will always have the <u>same potential difference</u> across them (because they're connected in parallel — see p.29).
4) The <u>pd</u> of the power supply is <u>shared out</u> between the thermistor and the loop made up of the fixed resistor and the fan according to their <u>resistances</u> — the <u>bigger</u> a component's resistance, the <u>more</u> of the pd it takes.
5) As the room gets hotter, the resistance of the thermistor <u>decreases</u> and it takes a <u>smaller share</u> of the pd from the power supply. So the pd across the fixed resistor and the fan <u>rises</u>, making the fan go faster.

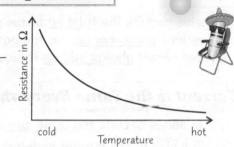

You can also connect the component <u>across the variable resistor</u> instead.

For example, if you connect a <u>bulb</u> in parallel to an <u>LDR</u>, the <u>pd</u> across both the LDR and the bulb will be <u>high</u> when it's <u>dark</u> and the LDR's resistance is <u>high</u>. The <u>greater the pd</u> across a component, the <u>more energy</u> it gets. So a <u>bulb</u> connected <u>across an LDR</u> would get <u>brighter</u> as the room got <u>darker</u>.

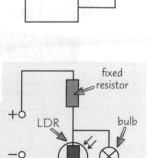

LDRs — Light Dependent Rabbits...

More odd circuit symbols, but at least we're getting into how different components are used in daily life — the next time your heating turns on automatically, you can be smug in your knowledge of thermistors.

Q1   Describe one everyday use for the following components:
    a) a LDR   b) a thermistor   [2 marks]

Series Circuits

There's a difference between connecting components in <u>series</u> and <u>parallel</u>. Make sure you learn it, and know the <u>rules</u> about what happens to <u>current</u>, <u>pd</u> and <u>resistance</u> in each case — read on for more series fun.

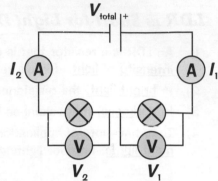

Series Circuits — All or Nothing

1) In <u>series circuits</u>, the different components are connected <u>in a line</u>, <u>end to end</u>, between the +ve and −ve of the power supply (except for <u>voltmeters</u>, which are always connected <u>in parallel</u>, but they don't count as part of the circuit).

2) If you remove or disconnect <u>one</u> component, the circuit is <u>broken</u> and they all <u>stop</u>. This is generally <u>not very handy</u>, and in practice <u>very few things</u> are connected in series.

3) You can use the following rules to <u>design</u> series circuits to <u>measure</u> <u>quantities</u> and test components (e.g. the <u>test circuit</u> on p.26 and the <u>sensing circuits</u> on p.27).

Potential Difference is Shared

In series circuits the <u>total pd</u> of the <u>supply</u> is <u>shared</u> between the various <u>components</u>. So the <u>potential differences</u> round a series circuit <u>always add up</u> to equal the <u>source pd</u>:

$$V_{total} = V_1 + V_2 + \ldots$$

Current is the Same Everywhere

1) In series circuits the <u>same current</u> flows through <u>all components</u>, i.e.:

$$I_1 = I_2 = \ldots$$

2) The <u>size</u> of the current is determined by the <u>total pd</u> of the cells and the <u>total resistance</u> of the circuit: i.e. $I = V \div R$.

Resistance Adds Up

1) In series circuits the <u>total resistance</u> of two components is just the <u>sum</u> of their resistances:

$$R_{total} = R_1 + R_2$$

2) This is because by <u>adding a resistor</u> in series, the two resistors have to <u>share</u> the total pd.

3) The potential difference across each resistor is <u>lower</u>, so the <u>current</u> through each resistor is also lower. In a series circuit, the current is the <u>same everywhere</u> so the total current in the circuit is <u>reduced</u> when a resistor is added. This means the total <u>resistance</u> of the circuit <u>increases</u>.

4) The <u>bigger</u> a component's <u>resistance</u>, the bigger its <u>share</u> of the <u>total potential difference</u>.

EXAMPLE: For the circuit diagram below, calculate the current passing through the circuit.

2 Ω   3 Ω

20 V

1) First find the <u>total resistance</u> by <u>adding</u> <u>together</u> the resistance of the two resistors.

2) Then <u>rearrange</u> $V = IR$ and <u>substitute</u> in the values you have.

$R_{total} = 2 + 3 = 5\ \Omega$

$I = V \div R$

$= 20 \div 5$

$= 4\ A$

Cell Potential Differences Add Up

1) There is a bigger pd when more cells are in series, if they're all <u>connected</u> the <u>same way</u>.

2) For example when two cells with a potential difference of 1.5 V are <u>connected in series</u> they supply **3 V** <u>between them</u>.

Series circuits — they're no laughing matter...

Get those rules straightened out in your head, then have a quick go at this question to test what you can remember.

Q1 Two 12 V cells are connected in series with a 2 Ω resistor, a 3 Ω resistor and a 7 Ω resistor. Calculate the current through the circuit. [5 marks]

Parallel Circuits

Parallel circuits are much more <u>sensible</u> than series circuits and so they're much more <u>common</u> in <u>real life</u>. All the electrics in your house will be wired in parallel circuits.

Parallel Circuits — Independence and Isolation

1) In <u>parallel circuits</u>, each component is <u>separately</u> connected to the +ve and −ve of the <u>supply</u> (except ammeters, which are <u>always</u> connected in <u>series</u>).

2) If you remove or disconnect <u>one</u> of them, it will <u>hardly affect</u> the others at all.

3) This is <u>obviously</u> how <u>most</u> things must be connected, for example in <u>cars</u> and in <u>household electrics</u>. You have to be able to switch everything on and off <u>separately</u>.

4) Everyday circuits often include a <u>mixture</u> of series and parallel parts.

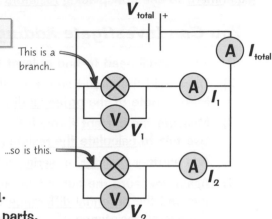

Potential Difference is the Same Across All Components

1) In parallel circuits <u>all</u> components get the <u>full source pd</u>, so the potential difference is the <u>same</u> across all components:

2) This means that <u>identical bulbs</u> connected in parallel will all be at the <u>same brightness</u>.

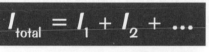

$$V_1 = V_2 = \ldots$$

Current is Shared Between Branches

1) In parallel circuits the <u>total current</u> flowing around the circuit is equal to the <u>total</u> of all the currents through the <u>separate components</u>.

2) In a parallel circuit, there are <u>junctions</u> where the current either <u>splits</u> or <u>rejoins</u>. The total current going <u>into</u> a junction has to equal the total current <u>leaving</u>.

3) If two <u>identical components</u> are connected in parallel then the <u>same current</u> will flow through each component.

$$I_{total} = I_1 + I_2 + \ldots$$

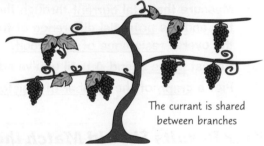

The currant is shared between branches

Adding a Resistor in Parallel Reduces the Total Resistance

1) If you have <u>two resistors in parallel</u>, their <u>total resistance</u> is <u>less than</u> the resistance of the <u>smallest</u> of the two resistors.

2) This can be tough to get your head around, but think about it like this:

- In <u>parallel</u>, both resistors have the <u>same potential difference</u> across them as the source.
- This means the '<u>pushing force</u>' making the current flow is the <u>same</u> as the <u>source pd</u> for each resistor that you add.
- But by adding another loop, the <u>current</u> has <u>more</u> than one direction to go in.
- This increases the <u>total current</u> that can flow around the circuit. Using $V = IR$, an <u>increase in current</u> means a <u>decrease</u> in the <u>total resistance</u> of the circuit.

A current shared (between identical components) *— is a current halved...*

Parallel circuits are a bit more complicated, but they're much more useful than series circuits, so get learning them.

Q1 Explain what happens to the current and resistance in a circuit containing a cell and a resistor when a second resistor is added in parallel. [2 marks]

Q2 Draw a circuit diagram for two filament lamps connected in parallel to a battery. Both of the lamps can be switched on and off without affecting each other. [3 marks]

PRACTICAL Investigating Resistance

You saw on page 25 how the length of the wire used in a circuit affects its resistance. Now it's time to do an <u>experiment</u> to see how placing <u>resistors</u> in series or in parallel can affect the resistance of the <u>whole circuit</u>.

You Can Investigate Adding Resistors in Series...

1) First, you'll need to find at least four <u>identical resistors</u>.

2) Then build the circuit shown on the right using <u>one</u> of the resistors. Make a note of the <u>potential difference</u> of the <u>battery</u> (*V*).

3) Measure the <u>current</u> through the circuit using the ammeter. Use this to <u>calculate the resistance</u> of the circuit using $R = V \div I$.

4) Add another <u>resistor</u>, in <u>series</u> with the first.

5) Again, measure the current through the circuit and use this and the <u>potential difference</u> of the battery to <u>calculate</u> the overall <u>resistance</u> of the circuit.

6) Repeat <u>steps 4 and 5</u> until you've added all of your resistors.

7) <u>Plot a graph</u> of the <u>number of resistors</u> against the <u>total resistance</u> of the circuit (see below).

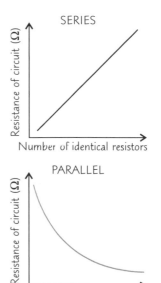

... or in Parallel

1) Using the <u>same equipment</u> as before (so the experiment is a <u>fair test</u>), build the same <u>initial circuit</u>.

2) Measure the <u>total current</u> through the circuit and <u>calculate the resistance</u> of the circuit using $R = V \div I$ (again, *V* is the potential difference of the <u>battery</u>).

3) Next, add another <u>resistor</u>, in <u>parallel</u> with the first.

4) Measure the <u>total current</u> through the circuit and use this and the <u>potential difference</u> of the battery to calculate the overall <u>resistance of the circuit</u>.

5) Repeat <u>steps 3 and 4</u> until you've added all of your resistors.

6) Plot a <u>graph</u> of the <u>number of resistors</u> in the circuit against the <u>total resistance</u>.

Your Results Should Match the Resistance Rules

1) You should find that adding resistors in <u>series increases</u> the total <u>resistance</u> of the circuit (adding a resistor <u>decreases</u> the total <u>current</u> through the circuit).

2) The <u>more</u> resistors you add, the <u>larger</u> the resistance of the whole circuit.

3) When you add resistors in <u>parallel</u>, the <u>total current</u> through the circuit <u>increases</u> — so the total resistance of the circuit has <u>decreased</u>.

4) The <u>more</u> resistors you add, the <u>smaller</u> the overall resistance becomes — as shown by the graph on the right.

5) These results <u>agree</u> with what you learnt about <u>resistance</u> in series and parallel circuits on pages 28 and 29.

SERIES

Resistance of circuit (Ω)

Number of identical resistors

PARALLEL

Resistance of circuit (Ω)

Number of identical resistors

I can't resist a good practical...

Nothing too hard on this page, which makes a nice change from all of those rules about circuits. Make sure you're completely happy building circuits from diagrams, before moving on to the fun world of mains electricity... wooo...

Q1   Draw a diagram of a single circuit that could be used to investigate the effect of adding resistors in parallel. Your circuit should include switches.   [1 mark]

Electricity in the Home

There are two types of electricity supply — <u>alternating</u> and <u>direct currents</u>. Read on for more about both...

Mains Supply is ac, Battery Supply is dc

1) There are two types of electricity supplies — <u>alternating current</u> (ac) and <u>direct current</u> (dc).

2) In <u>ac supplies</u> the current is <u>constantly</u> changing direction. Alternating currents are produced by <u>alternating voltages</u> (p.97) in which the <u>positive</u> and <u>negative</u> ends keep <u>alternating</u>.

3) The <u>UK mains supply</u> (the electricity in your home) is an ac supply at around <u>230 V</u>.

4) The frequency of the ac mains supply is <u>50 cycles per second</u> or <u>50 Hz</u> (hertz).

5) By contrast, cells and batteries supply <u>direct current</u> (dc).

6) <u>Direct current</u> is a current that is always flowing in the <u>same direction</u>.
It's created by a <u>direct voltage</u>.

Most Cables Have Three Separate Wires

1) Most electrical appliances are connected to the mains supply by <u>three-core</u> cables. This means that they have <u>three wires</u> inside them, each with a <u>core of copper</u> and a <u>coloured plastic coating</u>.

2) The <u>colour</u> of the insulation on each cable shows its <u>purpose</u>.

3) The colours are <u>always</u> the <u>same</u> for <u>every</u> appliance.
This is so that it is easy to tell the different wires <u>apart</u>.

4) You need to know the <u>colour</u> of each wire, what each of them is <u>for</u> and what their <u>pd</u> is:

1) <u>LIVE WIRE</u> — <u>brown</u>.
The live wire provides the <u>alternating potential difference</u> (at about <u>230 V</u>) from the mains supply

2) <u>NEUTRAL WIRE</u> — <u>blue</u>.
The neutral wire <u>completes</u> the circuit and carries away current — electricity normally flows <u>in</u> through the <u>live</u> wire and <u>out</u> through the <u>neutral</u> wire. It is around <u>0 V</u>.

3) <u>EARTH WIRE</u> — <u>green</u> and <u>yellow</u>.
It is for protecting the wiring, and for safety — it stops the appliance casing from <u>becoming live</u>. It doesn't usually carry a current — only when there's a <u>fault</u>. It's <u>also</u> at 0 V.

The Live Wire Can Give You an Electric Shock

1) Your <u>body</u> (just like the earth) is at <u>0 V</u>. This means that if you touch the <u>live wire</u>, a large <u>potential difference</u> is produced across your body and a <u>current</u> flows through <u>you</u>.

2) This causes a large <u>electric shock</u> which could injure or even kill you.

3) Even if a plug socket or a light switch is turned <u>off</u> (i.e. the switch is <u>open</u>) there is still a <u>danger</u> of an electric shock. A current isn't flowing but there's still a pd in the live wire. If you made <u>contact</u> with the live wire, your body would provide a <u>link</u> between the supply and the earth, so a current would flow <u>through you</u>.

4) <u>Any</u> connection between <u>live</u> and <u>earth</u> can be <u>dangerous</u>. If the link creates a <u>low resistance</u> path to earth, a huge current will flow, which could result in a fire.

Why are earth wires green and yellow — when mud is brown..?

Electricity is very useful, but it can also be very dangerous. Make sure you know the risks.

Q1   State the potential difference of: a) the live wire   b) the neutral wire   c) the earth wire.   [3 marks]

Power of Electrical Appliances

Energy is transferred between stores electrically (like you saw on page 11) by electrical appliances.

Energy is Transferred from Cells and Other Sources

1) You know from page 11 that a moving charge transfers energy. This is because the charge does work against the resistance of the circuit. (Work done is the same as energy transferred, p.53.)

2) Electrical appliances are designed to transfer energy to components in the circuit when a current flows.

Kettles transfer energy electrically from the mains ac supply to the thermal energy store of the heating element inside the kettle.

Energy is transferred electrically from the battery of a handheld fan to the kinetic energy store of the fan's motor.

3) Of course, no appliance transfers all energy completely usefully. The higher the current, the more energy is transferred to the thermal energy stores of the components (and then the surroundings). You can calculate the efficiency of any electrical appliance — see p.17.

Energy Transferred Depends on the Power

1) The total energy transferred by an appliance depends on how long the appliance is on for and its power.

2) The power of an appliance is the energy that it transfers per second. So the more energy it transfers in a given time, the higher its power.

This equation should be familiar from page 14.

3) The amount of energy transferred by electrical work is given by:

$$\text{Energy transferred (J)} = \text{Power (W)} \times \text{Time (s)} \qquad E = Pt$$

EXAMPLE: A 600 W microwave is used for 5 minutes. How long (in minutes) would a 750 W microwave take to do the same amount of work?

1) Calculate the energy transferred by the 600 W microwave in five minutes.

$E = Pt = 600 \times (5 \times 60)$
$= 180\,000$ J

Remember that the time must be in seconds.

2) Rearrange $E = Pt$ and sub in the energy you calculated and the power of the 750 W microwave.

$t = E \div P$
$= 180\,000 \div 750 = 240$ s

3) Convert the time back to minutes.

$240 \div 60 = 4$ minutes

So the 750 W microwave would take 4 minutes to do the same amount of work.

4) Appliances are often given a power rating — they're labelled with the maximum safe power that they can operate at. You can usually take this to be their maximum operating power.

5) The power rating tells you the maximum amount of energy transferred between stores per second when the appliance is in use.

6) This helps customers choose between models — the lower the power rating, the less electricity an appliance uses in a given time and so the cheaper it is to run.

7) But, a higher power doesn't necessarily mean that it transfers more energy usefully. An appliance may be more powerful than another, but less efficient, meaning that it might still only transfer the same amount of energy (or even less) to useful stores (see p.14).

Transfer this page to your useful knowledge store...

Get that equation for power hard-wired into your brain and then become a powerful physicist by practising it:

Q1   An appliance transfers 6000 J of energy in 30 seconds. Calculate its power.   [2 marks]

Q2   Calculate the difference in the amount of energy transferred by a 250 W TV and a 375 W TV when they are both used for two hours.   [4 marks]

More on Power

And we're not done yet. There are even more <u>power equations</u> for you to get your head around, how fun.

Potential Difference is Energy Transferred per Charge Passed

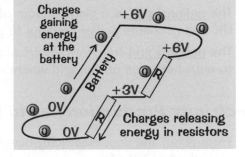

Charges gaining energy at the battery

Charges releasing energy in resistors

Battery

+6V

+6V

+3V

0V

0V

R

R

1) When an electrical <u>charge</u> goes through a <u>change</u> in potential difference, then <u>energy</u> is <u>transferred</u>.

2) Energy is <u>supplied</u> to the charge at the <u>power source</u> to 'raise' it through a potential.

3) The charge <u>gives up</u> this energy when it '<u>falls</u>' through any <u>potential drop</u> in <u>components</u> elsewhere in the circuit.

4) The formula is real simple:

Charge flow (C)

Energy transferred (J) — $E = QV$ — Potential difference (V)

5) That means that a battery with a <u>bigger pd</u> will supply <u>more energy</u> to the circuit for every <u>coulomb</u> of charge which flows round it, because the charge is raised up "<u>higher</u>" at the start.

**EXAMPLE:**

The motor in an electric toothbrush is attached to a 3 V battery. 140 C of charge passes through the circuit as it is used. Calculate the energy transferred.

$E = QV = 140 \times 3 = 420$ J

This energy is transferred to the kinetic energy store of the motor, as well as to the thermal energy stores of the surroundings.

Power Also Depends on Current and Potential Difference

1) As well as energy transferred in a given time, the <u>power</u> of an appliance can be found with:

Power (W) = Potential difference (V) × Current (A) $P = VI$

**EXAMPLE:**

A 1.0 kW hair dryer is connected to a 230 V supply. Calculate the current through the hair dryer. Give your answer to two significant figures.

1) <u>Rearrange</u> the equation for current. $I = P \div V$
2) Make sure your <u>units</u> are correct.   1.0 kW = 1000 W
3) Then just <u>stick in</u> the numbers that you have. $I = 1000 \div 230 = 4.34... = 4.3$ A (to 2 s.f.)

2) You can also find the power if you <u>don't know</u> the <u>potential difference</u>. To do this, stick $V = IR$ from page 25 into $P = VI$, which gives you: $P = I^2R$ Resistance (Ω)

You have the power — now use your potential...

I'm afraid the best way to learn all of this is to just practise using those equations again and again. Sorry.

Q1   Calculate the energy transferred from a 200 V source as 10 000 C of charge passes.   [2 marks]

Q2   An appliance is connected to a 12 V source. A current of 4.0 A flows through it. Calculate the power of the appliance.   [2 marks]

Q3   An appliance is connected to a 230 V mains supply and has a current of 10.0 A flowing through it. Calculate the resistance of the appliance.   [5 marks]

The National Grid

The national grid is a giant web of wires that covers the whole of Britain, getting electricity from power stations to homes everywhere. Whoever you pay for your electricity, it's the national grid that gets it to you.

Electricity is Distributed via the National Grid

1) The national grid is a giant system of cables and transformers (p.98) that covers the UK and connects power stations to consumers (anyone who is using electricity).

2) The national grid transfers electrical power from power stations anywhere on the grid (the supply) to anywhere else on the grid where it's needed (the demand) — e.g. homes and industry.

Electricity Production has to Meet Demand

1) Throughout the day, electricity usage (the demand) changes. Power stations have to produce enough electricity for everyone to have it when they need it.

2) They can predict when the most electricity will be used though. Demand increases when people get up in the morning, come home from school or work and when it starts to get dark or cold outside. Popular events like a sporting final being shown on TV could also cause a peak in demand.

3) Power stations often run at well below their maximum power output, so there's spare capacity to cope with a high demand, even if there's an unexpected shut-down of another station.

4) Lots of smaller power stations that can start up quickly are also kept in standby just in case.

The National Grid Uses a High Pd and a Low Current

1) To transmit the huge amount of power needed, you need either a high potential difference or a high current (as $P = VI$, from the previous page).

2) The problem with a high current is that you lose loads of energy as the wires heat up and energy is transferred to the thermal energy store of the surroundings.

3) It's much cheaper to boost the pd up really high (400 000 V) and keep the current as low as possible.

4) For a given power, increasing the pd decreases the current, which decreases the energy lost by heating the wires and the surroundings. This makes the national grid an efficient way of transferring energy.

Remember that power is the energy transferred in a given time, so a higher power means more energy transferred.

Potential Difference is Changed by a Transformer

1) To get the potential difference to 400 000 V to transmit power requires transformers as well as big pylons with huge insulators — but it's still cheaper.

2) The transformers have to step the potential difference up at one end, for efficient transmission, and then bring it back down to safe, usable levels at the other end.

For more on how transformers work, including a useful equation, have a look at page 98.

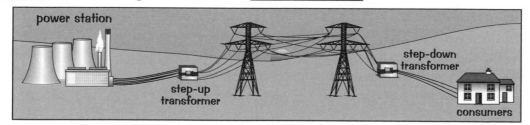

3) The potential difference is increased ('stepped up') using a step-up transformer.

4) It's then reduced again ('stepped down') for domestic use using a step-down transformer.

Transformers — NOT robots in disguise...

Think of this as 'transformers, part one'. You'll run into them again on page 98, but what's important here is that you understand how they're used in the national grid to reduce energy losses during transmission.

Q1   Explain why the national grid is efficient at transferring energy.
      Refer to the potential difference and current during transmission.

[4 marks]

Static Electricity

Static electricity is all about charges which are <u>not</u> free to move, e.g. in insulating materials. This causes them to build up in one place and it often ends with a <u>spark</u> or a <u>shock</u> when they do finally move.

Build-up of Static is Caused by Friction

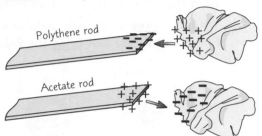

Polythene rod

Acetate rod

1) When certain <u>insulating</u> materials are <u>rubbed</u> together, negatively charged electrons will be <u>scraped off one</u> and <u>dumped</u> on the other.

2) This will leave the materials <u>electrically charged</u>, with a <u>positive</u> static charge on one and an <u>equal negative</u> static charge on the other.

3) <u>Which way</u> the electrons are transferred <u>depends</u> on the <u>two materials</u> involved.

4) The classic examples are <u>polythene</u> and <u>acetate</u> rods being rubbed with a <u>cloth duster</u> (shown on the right).

Only Electrons Move — Never Positive Charges

<u>Watch out for this in exams.</u> Both +ve and –ve electrostatic charges are only ever produced by the movement of <u>electrons</u>. The positive charges <u>definitely do not move!</u>

A positive static charge is always caused by electrons <u>moving</u> away elsewhere. The material that <u>loses</u> the electrons loses some negative charge, and is <u>left with an equal positive charge</u>. Don't forget!

Too Much Static Causes Sparks

For more on how sparks actually jump across gaps, see the next page.

1) As <u>electric charge</u> builds on an object, the <u>potential difference</u> between the object and the earth (which is at <u>0 V</u>) increases.

2) If the potential difference gets <u>large enough</u>, electrons can <u>jump</u> across the <u>gap</u> between the charged object and the earth — this is the <u>spark</u>.

3) They can also <u>jump</u> to any <u>earthed conductor</u> that is nearby — which is why <u>you</u> can get <u>static shocks</u> getting out of a car. A charge builds up on the car's <u>metal frame</u>, and when you touch the car, the <u>charge</u> travels <u>through you</u> to earth.

4) This <u>usually</u> happens when the gap is fairly <u>small</u>. (But not always — <u>lightning</u> is just a really big spark.)

Like Charges Repel, Opposite Charges Attract

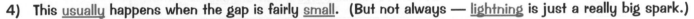

1) This is <u>easy</u> and, I'd have thought, <u>kind of obvious</u>. When two electrically charged objects are brought close together they <u>exert a force</u> on one another.

2) Two things with <u>opposite</u> electric charges are <u>attracted</u> to each other, while two things with the <u>same</u> electric charge will <u>repel</u> each other.

3) These forces get <u>weaker</u> the <u>further apart</u> the two things are.

4) These forces will cause the objects to <u>move</u> if they are able to do so. This is known as <u>electrostatic attraction</u> / <u>repulsion</u> and is a <u>non-contact</u> force (the objects don't need to touch, p.51).

5) One way to see this force is to <u>suspend</u> a <u>rod</u> with a <u>known charge</u> from a piece of string (so it is free to <u>move</u>). Placing an object with the <u>same charge</u> nearby will <u>repel</u> the rod — the rod will <u>move away</u> from the object. An <u>oppositely charged</u> object will cause the rod to move <u>towards</u> the object.

Stay away from electrons — they're a negative influence...

Electrons jumping about the place and giving us all shocks, the cheeky so-and-sos.

Q1   Jake removes his jumper in a dark room. As he does so, he hears a crackling noise and sees tiny sparks of light between his jumper and his shirt. Explain the cause of this.   [3 marks]

Electric Fields

Electric fields — much less green and much more shocking than the fields you're used to.

Electric Charges Create an Electric Field

1) An electric field is created around any electrically charged object.

2) The closer to the object you get, the stronger the field is.
   (And the further you are from it, the weaker it is.)

3) You can show an electric field around an object using field lines.
   For example you can draw the field lines for an isolated, charged sphere:

Isolated means it's not interacting with anything.

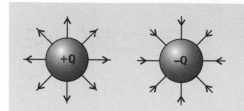

- Electric field lines go from positive to negative.
- They're always at a right angle to the surface.
- The closer together the lines are, the stronger the field is — you can see that the further from a charge you go, the further apart the lines are and so the weaker the field is.

Charged Objects in an Electric Field feel a Force

1) When a charged object is placed in the electric field of another object, it feels a force.

2) This force causes the attraction or repulsion you saw on the previous page.

3) The force is caused by the electric fields of each charged object interacting with each other.

4) The force on an object is linked to the strength of the electric field it is in.

5) As you increase the distance between the charged objects, the strength of the field decreases and the force between them gets smaller.

Two oppositely charged particles

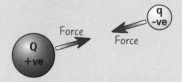

1) The electric field of Q interacts with the electric field of q.

2) This causes forces to act on both Q and q.

3) These forces move q and Q closer together.

Sparking Can Be Explained By Electric Fields

1) Sparks are caused when there is a high enough potential difference between a charged object and the earth (or an earthed object).

2) A high potential difference causes a strong electric field between the charged object and the earthed object.

3) The strong electric field causes electrons in the air particles to be removed (known as ionisation).

4) Air is normally an insulator, but when it is ionised it is much more conductive, so a current can flow through it. This is the spark.

You're one bright spark if you've managed to finish this topic...

And we've saved the toughest 'til last. Re-read this page to really get your head around electric fields. Remember that field lines always point from positive to negative and that the closer they are, the stronger the field is.

Q1   Draw the field lines surrounding an isolated, positively charged sphere.   [2 marks]

Q2   Explain what happens to the force acting on a negative charge as it moves closer to a positively charged object.   [3 marks]

Revision Questions for Topic 2

Congratulations! You've battled to the end of <u>Topic 2</u> — now see how much you've learnt.

- Try these questions and <u>tick off each one</u> when you <u>get it right</u>.
- When you've done <u>all the questions</u> under a heading and are <u>completely happy</u> with it, tick it off.

Circuit Basics (p.24-27) ☑

1) Define current and state an equation that links current, charge and time, with units for each.
2) What is meant by potential difference and resistance in a circuit?
3) Draw the circuit symbols for: a cell, a filament lamp, a diode, a fuse and an **LDR**.
4) What is the equation that links potential difference, current and resistance?
5) Explain how you would investigate how the length of a wire affects its resistance.
6) What is an ohmic conductor?
7) Draw a circuit that could be used to investigate how the resistance of a filament bulb changes with the current through it.
8) Name one linear component and one non-linear component.
9) Explain how the resistance of an LDR varies with light intensity.
10) What happens to the resistance of a thermistor as it gets hotter?

Series and Parallel Circuits (p.28-30) ☑

11) True or false? Potential difference is shared between components in a series circuit.
12) How does the current through each component vary in a series circuit?
13) How does potential difference vary between components connected in parallel?
14) Explain why adding resistors in parallel decreases the total resistance of a circuit, but adding them in series increases the total resistance.
15) Describe an experiment to investigate how adding resistors in series and parallel affects the total resistance of the circuit.

Electricity in the Home (p.31) ☑

16) True or false? Mains supply electricity is an alternating current.
17) What is the potential difference and the frequency of the UK mains supply?
18) Name and give the colours of the three wires in a three-core cable. Why are they colour coded?
19) Give the potential differences for the three wires in a three-core mains cable.
20) Explain why touching a live wire is dangerous.

Power and the National Grid (p.32-34) ☑

21) State three equations that can be used to calculate electrical power.
22) What is the power rating of an appliance?
23) Explain why electricity is transferred by the national grid at a high pd but low current.
24) What are the functions of step-up and step-down transformers?

Static Electricity and Electric Fields (p.35-36) ☑

25) How does rubbing of materials cause static electricity to build up?
26) True or false? Two positive charges attract each other.
27) In which direction do the arrows on electric field lines point?
28) Using the concept of electric fields, explain how a build up of static electricity can cause a spark.

Density of Materials

The <u>particle model of matter</u> says that everything is made up of <u>lots of tiny particles</u>. It's <u>dead useful</u>.

The Particle Model can Explain Density and the Three States of Matter

Density is a measure of the '<u>compactness</u>' of a substance. It relates the <u>mass</u> of a substance to how much <u>space</u> it takes up (i.e. it's a substance's <u>mass</u> per <u>unit volume</u>).

$$\text{Density (kg/m}^3) = \frac{\text{mass (kg)}}{\text{volume (m}^3)}$$

The symbol for density is a Greek letter rho (ρ). Density can also be given in g/cm³. 1 g/cm³ = 1000 kg/m³.

$\dfrac{m}{\rho \times V}$

1) The density of an object depends on <u>what it's made of</u> and how its <u>particles</u> are <u>arranged</u>.

2) A <u>dense</u> material has its particles <u>packed tightly</u> together. The particles in a <u>less dense</u> material are more <u>spread out</u> — if you <u>compressed</u> the material, its particles would move <u>closer together</u>, and it would become <u>more dense</u>. (You <u>wouldn't</u> be changing its <u>mass</u>, but you <u>would</u> be <u>decreasing</u> its <u>volume</u>.)

The <u>three states of matter</u> are <u>solid</u> (e.g. ice), <u>liquid</u> (e.g. water) and <u>gas</u> (e.g. water vapour). The <u>particles</u> of a substance in each state are the same — only the <u>arrangement</u> and <u>energy</u> of the particles are different.

SOLIDS — <u>strong</u> forces of attraction hold the particles close together in a <u>fixed</u>, <u>regular</u> arrangement. The particles don't have much energy so they can only <u>vibrate</u> about their fixed positions. The <u>density</u> is generally <u>highest</u> in this state as the particles are <u>closest together</u>.

LIQUIDS — there are <u>weaker</u> forces of attraction between the particles. The particles are <u>close</u> together, but can <u>move past</u> each other, and form <u>irregular arrangements</u>. They have <u>more</u> energy than the particles in a solid — they move in <u>random directions</u> at <u>low speeds</u>. Liquids are generally <u>less dense</u> than solids.

GASES — there are almost <u>no forces</u> of attraction between the particles. The particles have <u>more energy</u> than in liquids and solids — they're <u>free to move</u>, and travel in <u>random directions</u> at <u>high speeds</u>. Gases are generally <u>less dense</u> than liquids — they have <u>low</u> densities.

You Need to be Able to Measure Density in Different Ways | PRACTICAL

To find the density of a solid object

1) Use a <u>balance</u> to measure its <u>mass</u> (see p.104).

2) If it's a <u>regular</u> solid, start by measuring its <u>length</u>, <u>width</u> and <u>height</u> with an <u>appropriate</u> piece of equipment (e.g. a <u>ruler</u>). Then calculate its <u>volume</u> using the relevant <u>formula</u> for that shape.

3) For an irregular solid, you can find its volume by <u>submerging</u> it in a <u>eureka can</u> filled with water. The water <u>displaced</u> by the object will be <u>transferred</u> to the <u>measuring cylinder</u>:

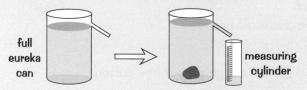

full eureka can → measuring cylinder

4) Record the <u>volume</u> of water in the measuring cylinder. This is the <u>volume</u> of the <u>object</u>.

5) Plug the object's <u>mass</u> and <u>volume</u> into the <u>formula</u> above to find its <u>density</u>.

To find the density of a liquid

1) Place a <u>measuring cylinder</u> on a balance and <u>zero</u> the balance.

2) Pour <u>10 ml</u> of the liquid into the measuring cylinder (see p.105) and record the liquid's <u>mass</u>.

3) Pour <u>another 10 ml</u> into the measuring cylinder, <u>repeating</u> the process until the cylinder is full and recording the <u>total</u> <u>volume</u> and <u>mass</u> each time.

4) For each measurement, use the <u>formula</u> to find the <u>density</u>. (Remember that 1 ml = 1 cm³.)

5) Finally, take an <u>average</u> of your calculated densities. This will give you a value for the <u>density</u> of the <u>liquid</u>.

The volume of a cube is equal to length × width × height. Make sure you know the formulas for basic shapes.

Who can measure volume — the eureka can can, oh the eureka can can...

Remember — density is all about how tightly packed the particles in a substance are. Nice and simple really.

Q1   A cube has edges of length 1.5 cm and average density 3500 kg/m³. What is its mass?   [5 marks]

Internal Energy and Changes of State

This page is all about heating things. Take a look at your specific heat capacity notes (p.13) before you start — you need to understand it and be able to be able to use $\Delta E = mc\Delta\theta$ for this topic too I'm afraid.

Internal Energy is the Energy Stored by the Particles That Make Up a System

1) The particles in a system vibrate or move around — they have energy in their kinetic energy stores.

2) They also have energy in their potential energy stores due to their positions.

3) The energy stored in a system is stored by its particles (atoms and molecules). The internal energy of a system is the total energy that its particles have in their kinetic and potential energy stores.

4) Heating the system transfers energy to its particles (they gain energy in their kinetic stores and move faster), increasing the internal energy.

5) This leads to a change in temperature or a change in state. If the temperature changes, the size of the change depends on the mass of the substance, what it's made of (its specific heat capacity) and the energy input. Make sure you remember all of the stuff on specific heat capacity from p.13, particularly how to use the formula.

6) A change in state occurs if the substance is heated enough — the particles will have enough energy in their kinetic energy stores to break the bonds holding them together.

A Change of State Conserves Mass

1) When you heat a liquid, it boils (or evaporates) and becomes a gas. When you heat a solid, it melts and becomes a liquid. These are both changes of state.

2) The state can also change due to cooling. The particles lose energy and form bonds.

3) The changes of state are:

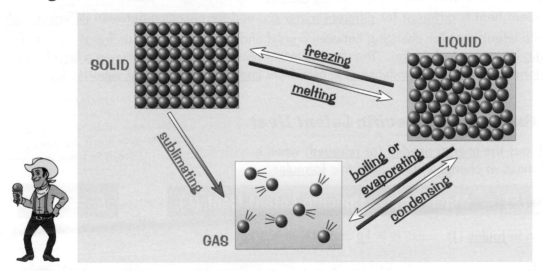

4) A change of state is a physical change (rather than a chemical change). This means you don't end up with a new substance — it's the same substance as you started with, just in a different form.

5) If you reverse a change of state (e.g. freeze a substance that has been melted), the substance will return to its original form and get back its original properties.

6) The number of particles doesn't change — they're just arranged differently. This means mass is conserved — none of it is lost when the substance changes state.

Breaking Bonds — Blofeld never quite manages it...

I'll say it one more time — have a look back over your specific heat capacity notes. They'll really help you understand all this stuff on temperature changes and internal energy. Now don't say I didn't warn you...

Q1 During an experiment, a solid is heated until it melts into a liquid. Explain how heating the solid causes this change of state. [3 marks]

Topic 3 — Particle Model of Matter

Specific Latent Heat

If you heat up a pan of water on the stove, the water never gets any hotter than 100 °C. You can <u>carry on heating it up</u>, but the <u>temperature won't rise</u>. How come, you say? It's all to do with <u>latent heat</u>...

A Change of State Requires Energy

1) When a substance is <u>melting</u> or <u>boiling</u>, you're still putting in <u>energy</u> and so <u>increasing</u> the <u>internal energy</u>, but the energy's used for <u>breaking intermolecular bonds</u> rather than raising the temperature. There are <u>flat spots</u> on the heating graph where <u>energy</u> is being <u>transferred</u> by heating but not being used to change the temperature.

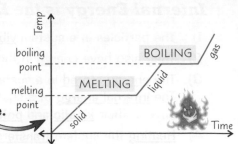

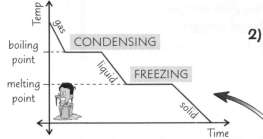

2) When a substance is <u>condensing</u> or <u>freezing</u>, bonds are <u>forming</u> between particles, which <u>releases</u> energy. This means the <u>internal energy decreases</u>, but the <u>temperature doesn't go down</u> until all the substance has turned to liquid (condensing) or a solid (freezing). The <u>flat parts</u> of the graph show this energy transfer.

3) The <u>energy needed</u> to change the state of a substance is called <u>latent heat</u>.

Specific Latent Heat is the Energy Needed to Change the State of a 1 kg Mass

1) The <u>specific latent heat</u> (SLH) of a substance is the <u>amount of energy</u> needed to <u>change 1 kg</u> of it from <u>one state to another without changing its temperature</u>.

2) For <u>cooling</u>, specific latent heat is the energy <u>released</u> by a change in state.

3) Specific latent heat is <u>different</u> for <u>different materials</u>, and for changing between <u>different states</u>.

4) The specific latent heat for changing between a <u>solid</u> and a <u>liquid</u> (<u>melting</u> or <u>freezing</u>) is called the <u>specific latent heat of fusion</u>. The specific latent heat for changing between a <u>liquid</u> and a <u>gas</u> (<u>evaporating</u>, <u>boiling</u> or <u>condensing</u>) is called the <u>specific latent heat of vaporisation</u>.

There's a Formula for Specific Latent Heat

Don't get confused with specific heat capacity (p.13), which relates to a temperature rise of 1 °C. Specific latent heat is about changes of state where there's no temperature change.

You can work out the <u>energy needed</u> (or <u>released</u>) when a substance of mass m changes state using this <u>formula</u>:

> Energy (E) = Mass (m) × Specific Latent Heat (L)   or: $E = mL$

Energy is given in <u>joules</u> (J), mass is in <u>kg</u> and SLH is in <u>J/kg</u>.

EXAMPLE:

The specific latent heat of vaporisation for water (boiling) is 2 260 000 J/kg. How much energy is needed to completely boil 1.50 kg of water at 100 °C?

1) Just plug the numbers into the <u>formula</u>.
2) The units are <u>joules</u> because it's <u>energy</u>.

$E = mL$
$= 1.50 × 2\,260\,000$
$= 3\,390\,000$ J

If you're finding mass or SLH, you'll need to rearrange. Here's the formula triangle.

My specific latent heat of revision* is 500 J/kg...

When it comes to the specific latent heat of vaporisation and fusion, the formula's the same, but the process is different. Make sure you understand which process you're actually looking at — you don't want to get caught out.

Q1 The SLH of fusion for a particular substance is 120 000 J/kg. How much energy is needed to melt 250 g of the substance when it is already at its melting temperature? [2 marks]

*the amount of energy required to turn 1 kg of revision notes into a top grade

Particle Motion in Gases

The particle model helps explain how temperature, pressure, volume and energy in kinetic stores are all related.

Average Energy in Kinetic Stores is Related to Temperature

1) The particles in a gas are constantly moving with random directions and speeds.
   If you increase the temperature of a gas, you transfer energy into the
   kinetic energy stores of its particles (you saw this on p.39).

2) The temperature of a gas is related to the average energy in the kinetic energy stores of the
   particles in the gas. The higher the temperature, the higher the average energy.

3) So as you increase the temperature of a gas, the average speed of its particles increases.
   This is because the energy in the particles' kinetic energy stores is $\frac{1}{2}mv^2$ — p.12.

Colliding Gas Particles Create Pressure

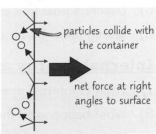

particles collide with the container

net force at right angles to surface

1) As gas particles move about at high speeds, they bang into each other and
   whatever else happens to get in the way. When they collide with something,
   they exert a force (and so a pressure — p.58) on it. In a sealed container,
   the outward gas pressure is the total force exerted by all of the
   particles in the gas on a unit area of the container walls.

2) Faster particles and more frequent collisions both lead to an increase in net force, and so gas pressure.
   Increasing temperature will increase the speed, and so the pressure (if volume is kept constant).

3) Alternatively, if temperature is constant, increasing the volume of a gas means the particles get
   more spread out and hit the walls of the container less often. The gas pressure decreases.

4) Pressure and volume are inversely proportional — when volume goes up, pressure goes down
   (and when volume decreases, pressure increases). For a gas of fixed mass at a constant temperature,
   the relationship is:

$$pV = \text{constant}$$

p = pressure, in pascals (Pa)
V = volume (m³)

See page 58 for more on pressure.

A Change in Pressure can Cause a Change in Volume

1) The pressure of a gas causes a net outwards force at right angles to the surface of its container.

2) There is also a force on the outside of the container due to the pressure of the gas around it.

3) If a container can easily change its size (e.g. a balloon), then any change in these pressures
   will cause the container to compress or expand, due to the overall force.

E.g. if a helium balloon is released, it rises. Atmospheric pressure decreases with
height (p.59), so the pressure outside the balloon decreases. This causes the balloon
to expand until the pressure inside drops to the same as the atmospheric pressure.

Doing Work on a Gas Can Increase its Temperature

There's more about doing work on p.53.

1) If you transfer energy by applying a force, then you do work. Doing work
   on a gas increases its internal energy, which can increase its temperature.

2) You can do work on a gas mechanically, e.g. with a bike pump. The gas
   applies pressure to the plunger of the pump, and so exerts a force on it.
   Work has to be done against this force to push down the plunger.

3) This transfers energy to the kinetic energy stores of the gas particles, increasing the
   temperature. If the pump is connected to a tyre, you should feel it getting warmer.

Don't let the pressure of exams get to you...

A bike pump at a desk. Does it get any better? Yep — here's a question...

Q1   3.5 m³ of a gas is at a pressure of 520 Pa. It is compressed to a volume of 1 m³
      at a constant temperature. What is the new pressure of the gas?   [3 marks]

Revision Questions for Topic 3

Topic 3 — all in all, quite a nice little topic. Have a go at this page to see how well you've understood it.
*   Try these questions and tick off each one when you get it right.
*   When you've done all the questions under a heading and are completely happy with it, tick it off.

Density of Materials (p.38) ☑

1) What is the formula for density?
2) What are the units of density?
3) What are the three states of matter?
4) For each state of matter, describe the arrangement of the particles.
5) Describe how you could find the volume of an irregular solid object.
6) Briefly describe an experiment to find the density of a liquid.

Internal Energy and Changes of State (p.39-40) ☑

7) What is internal energy?
8) What happens to the particles in a substance when that substance is heated?
9) Name the five changes of state.
10) Is a change of state a physical change or a chemical change?
11) True or false? Mass stays the same when a substance changes state.
12) Explain the cause of the flat sections on a graph of temperature against time for a substance being heated.
13) Sketch a graph of temperature against time for a gas being cooled. Your graph should show the points that the gas turns into a liquid and that the liquid turns into a solid.
14) Define specific latent heat.
15) Give a formula for specific latent heat.

Particle Motion in Gases (p.41) ☑

16) Explain how a gas in a sealed container exerts a pressure on the walls of the container.
17) A sealed container of gas is kept at a constant volume. The gas is heated. What happens to the pressure of the gas? Explain why.
18) For a fixed mass of gas at a constant temperature, what is the relationship between pressure and volume?
19) True or false? For a gas at constant temperature, increasing the volume of the gas will also increase its pressure.
20) A balloon containing a fixed mass of helium gas is moved from an area of high atmospheric pressure to one of low atmospheric pressure. What will happen to the volume of helium in the balloon?
21) Explain why blowing up a football with a pump causes the ball to warm up.

Developing the Model of the Atom

All this started with a Greek fella called Democritus in the 5th Century BC. He thought that all matter, whatever it was, was made up of identical lumps called "atomos". And that's as far as it got until the 1800s...

Rutherford Replaced the Plum Pudding Model with the Nuclear Model...

1) In 1804 John Dalton agreed with Democritus that matter was made up of tiny spheres ("atoms") that couldn't be broken up, but he reckoned that each element was made up of a different type of "atom".

2) Nearly 100 years later, J. J. Thomson discovered particles called electrons that could be removed from atoms. So Dalton's theory wasn't quite right. Thomson suggested atoms were spheres of positive charge with tiny negative electrons stuck in them like fruit in a plum pudding — the plum pudding model.

3) However, in 1909, scientists in Rutherford's lab tried firing a beam of alpha particles (see p.44) at thin gold foil — this was the alpha scattering experiment. From the plum pudding model, they expected the particles to pass straight through the gold sheet, or only be slightly deflected. But although most of the particles did go straight through the sheet, some were deflected more than expected, and a few were deflected back the way they had come — something the plum pudding model couldn't explain.

4) Because a few alpha particles were deflected back, the scientists realised that most of the mass of the atom must be concentrated at the centre in a tiny nucleus. This nucleus must also have a positive charge, since it repelled the positive alpha particles.

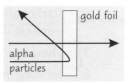

5) They also realised that because nearly all the alpha particles passed straight through, most of an atom is just empty space. This was the first nuclear model of the atom.

...Which Developed into the Current Model of the Atom

1) The nuclear model that resulted from the alpha particle scattering experiment was a positively charged nucleus surrounded by a cloud of negative electrons.

2) Niels Bohr said that electrons orbiting the nucleus do so at certain distances called energy levels. His theoretical calculations agreed with experimental data.

3) Evidence from further experiments changed the model to have a nucleus made up of a group of particles (protons) which all had the same positive charge that added up to the overall charge of the nucleus.

4) About 20 years after the idea of a nucleus was accepted, in 1932, James Chadwick proved the existence of the neutron, which explained the imbalance between the atomic and mass numbers (page 44).

| The Current Model of the Atom |
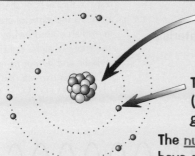

The nucleus is tiny but it makes up most of the mass of the atom. It contains protons (which are positively charged — they have a +1 relative charge) and neutrons (which are neutral, with a relative charge of 0) — which gives it an overall positive charge. Its radius is about 10 000 times smaller than the radius of the atom.

The rest of the atom is mostly empty space. Negative electrons (relative charge −1) whizz round the outside of the nucleus really fast. They give the atom its overall size — the radius of an atom is about 1×10^{-10} m.

The number of protons = the number of electrons, as protons and electrons have an equal but opposite charge and atoms have no overall charge.

Electrons in energy levels can move within (or sometimes leave) the atom. If they gain energy by absorbing EM radiation (p.76) they move to a higher energy level, further from the nucleus. If they release EM radiation, they move to a lower energy level that is closer to the nucleus. If one or more outer electrons leaves the atom, the atom becomes a positively charged ion.

We're currently pretty happy with this model, but there's no saying it won't change. Just like for the plum pudding, new experiments sometimes mean we have to change or completely get rid of current models.

These models don't have anything on my miniature trains...

This is science in action folks — as new evidence came along, the model of the atom was changed and updated.

Q1   a) Describe the current model of the atom.   [4 marks]
      b) State the radius of an atom and describe how this compares to the size of its nucleus.   [2 marks]

Isotopes and Nuclear Radiation

<u>Isotopes</u> and <u>ionisation</u>. They sound <u>similar</u>, but they're totally <u>different</u>, so read this page carefully.

Isotopes are Different Forms of the Same Element

1) All atoms of each <u>element</u> have a <u>set number</u> of <u>protons</u> (so each nucleus has a given <u>positive charge</u>). The <u>number</u> of protons in an atom is its <u>atomic number</u>.

2) The <u>mass number</u> of an atom (the <u>mass</u> of the <u>nucleus</u>) is the <u>number of protons</u> + the <u>number of neutrons</u> in its nucleus.

3) <u>Isotopes</u> of an element are atoms with the <u>same</u> number of <u>protons</u> (the same <u>atomic number</u>, and so the same <u>charge</u> on the <u>nucleus</u>) but a different number of <u>neutrons</u> (a different <u>mass number</u>). E.g. $^{18}_{8}O$ is an <u>isotope</u> of oxygen.

4) <u>All</u> elements have different isotopes, but there are usually only one or two <u>stable</u> ones.

5) The other <u>unstable</u> isotopes tend to <u>decay</u> into <u>other elements</u> and give out <u>radiation</u> as they try to become <u>more stable</u>. This process is called <u>radioactive decay</u>.

6) Radioactive substances <u>spit out</u> one or more types of <u>ionising</u> radiation from their nucleus — the ones you need to know are <u>alpha</u>, <u>beta</u> and <u>gamma</u> radiation.

7) They can also release <u>neutrons</u> (n) when they decay, as they <u>rebalance</u> their <u>atomic</u> and <u>mass</u> numbers.

8) Ionising radiation is radiation that <u>knocks electrons off</u> atoms, creating <u>positive ions</u>. The <u>ionising power</u> of a radiation source is <u>how easily</u> it can do this.

> Every oxygen atom has 8 protons.
>
> Mass number — $^{16}_{8}O$ — Element symbol (oxygen)
> Atomic number
>
> All atoms can be shown with this notation.

$^{14}_{7}N$

Alpha Particles are Helium Nuclei

1) Alpha radiation is when an <u>alpha particle</u> (α) is emitted from the nucleus. An α-particle is <u>two neutrons</u> and <u>two protons</u> (like a <u>helium nucleus</u>).

2) They <u>don't</u> penetrate very far into materials and are <u>stopped quickly</u> — they can only travel a <u>few cm in air</u> and are <u>absorbed</u> by a sheet of <u>paper</u>.

3) Because of their size they are <u>strongly ionising</u>.

> Alpha radiation is used in smoke detectors — it <u>ionises</u> air particles, causing a <u>current</u> to flow. If there is smoke in the air, it <u>binds</u> to the ions — meaning the current stops and the alarm sounds.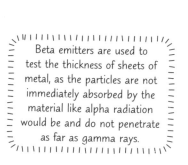

Beta Particles are High-Speed Electrons  e⁻

1) A <u>beta particle</u> (β) is simply a <u>fast-moving</u> <u>electron</u> released by the nucleus. Beta particles have virtually <u>no mass</u> and a charge of –1.

2) They are <u>moderately ionising</u>. They <u>penetrate moderately</u> far into materials before colliding and have a <u>range in air</u> of a <u>few metres</u>. They are <u>absorbed</u> by a sheet of <u>aluminium</u> (around <u>5 mm</u>).

3) For every <u>beta particle</u> emitted, a <u>neutron</u> in the nucleus has <u>turned into</u> a <u>proton</u> (page 45).

> Beta emitters are used to test the thickness of sheets of metal, as the particles are not immediately absorbed by the material like alpha radiation would be and do not penetrate as far as gamma rays.

Gamma Rays are EM Waves with a Short Wavelength

1) <u>Gamma rays</u> (γ) are waves of <u>electromagnetic radiation</u> (p.76) released by the nucleus.

2) They <u>penetrate far into materials</u> without being stopped and will travel a <u>long distance</u> through <u>air</u>.

3) This means they are <u>weakly</u> ionising because they tend to <u>pass through</u> rather than collide with atoms. Eventually they <u>hit something</u> and do <u>damage</u>.

4) They can be <u>absorbed</u> by thick sheets of <u>lead</u> or metres of <u>concrete</u>.

> Uses of gamma rays are on p.48 and p.80.

Ionising radiation — good for getting creases out of your clothes...

Knowing different kinds of radiation and what can absorb them usually bags you a few easy marks in an exam.

Q1   In the medical industry, radiation is directed at medical equipment sealed in packaging. The radiation sterilises the equipment. Explain whether alpha radiation would be suitable for this use.   [2 marks]

Nuclear Equations

Nuclear equations show radioactive decay and once you get the hang of them they're dead easy. Get going.

Mass and Atomic Numbers Have to Balance

1) Nuclear equations are a way of showing radioactive decay by using element symbols (p.44).

2) They're written in the form: atom before decay → atom after decay + radiation emitted.

3) There is one golden rule to remember:
the total mass and atomic numbers must be equal on both sides.

Alpha Decay Decreases the Charge and Mass of the Nucleus $\quad{}^{4}_{2}\text{He}$

1) Remember, alpha particles are made up of two protons and two neutrons. So when an atom emits an alpha particle, its atomic number reduces by 2 and its mass number reduces by 4.

2) A proton is positively charged and a neutron is neutral, so the charge of the nucleus decreases.

3) In nuclear equations, an alpha particle can be written as a helium nucleus: ${}^{4}_{2}\text{He}$.

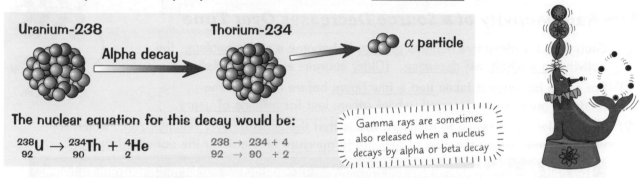

Uranium-238 — Alpha decay → Thorium-234 → α particle

The nuclear equation for this decay would be:

$${}^{238}_{92}\text{U} \rightarrow {}^{234}_{90}\text{Th} + {}^{4}_{2}\text{He}$$

$$238 \rightarrow 234 + 4$$
$$92 \rightarrow 90 + 2$$

Gamma rays are sometimes also released when a nucleus decays by alpha or beta decay

Beta Decay Increases the Charge of the Nucleus $\quad{}^{0}_{-1}\text{e}$

1) When beta decay occurs, a neutron in the nucleus turns into a proton and releases a fast-moving electron (the beta particle).

2) The number of protons in the nucleus has increased by 1. This increases the positive charge of the nucleus (the atomic number).

3) Because the nucleus has lost a neutron and gained a proton during beta decay, the mass of the nucleus doesn't change (protons and neutrons have the same mass).

4) A beta particle is written as ${}^{0}_{-1}\text{e}$ in nuclear equations.

In both alpha and beta emissions, a new element will be formed, as the number of protons (atomic number) changes.

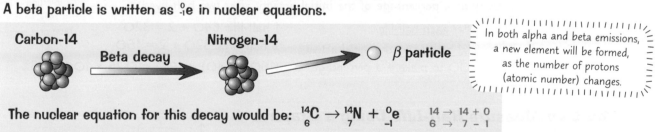

Carbon-14 — Beta decay → Nitrogen-14 → β particle

The nuclear equation for this decay would be: ${}^{14}_{6}\text{C} \rightarrow {}^{14}_{7}\text{N} + {}^{0}_{-1}\text{e}$

$$14 \rightarrow 14 + 0$$
$$6 \rightarrow 7 - 1$$

Gamma Rays Don't Change the Charge or Mass of the Nucleus

1) Gamma rays are a way of getting rid of excess energy from a nucleus.

2) This means that there is no change to the atomic mass or atomic number of the atom.

Keep balanced during revision and practise nuclear equations...

Nuclear equations are simple, but that doesn't mean you shouldn't practise them. Try these questions on for size.

Q1   What type of radiation is given off in this decay? ${}^{8}_{3}\text{Li} \rightarrow {}^{8}_{4}\text{Be}$ + radiation.   [1 mark]

Q2   Write the nuclear equation for ${}^{219}_{86}\text{Rn}$ decaying to polonium (Po) by emitting an alpha particle.   [3 marks]

Half-life

How quickly unstable nuclei decay is measured using activity and half-life — two very important terms.

Radioactivity is a Totally Random Process

1) Radioactive substances give out radiation from the nuclei of their atoms — no matter what.

2) This radiation can be measured with a Geiger-Muller tube and counter, which records the count-rate — the number of radiation counts reaching it per second.

3) Radioactive decay is entirely random. So you can't predict exactly which nucleus in a sample will decay next, or when any one of them will decay.

4) But you can find out the time it takes for the amount of radiation emitted by a source to halve, this is known as the half-life. It can be used to make predictions about radioactive sources, even though their decays are random.

5) Half-life can be used to find the rate at which a source decays — its ACTIVITY. Activity is measured in becquerels, Bq (where 1 Bq is 1 decay per second).

The Radioactivity of a Source Decreases Over Time

1) Each time a radioactive nucleus decays to become a stable nucleus, the activity as a whole will decrease. (Older sources emit less radiation.)

2) For some isotopes it takes just a few hours before nearly all the unstable nuclei have decayed, whilst others last for millions of years.

3) The problem with trying to measure this is that the activity never reaches zero, which is why we have to use the idea of half-life to measure how quickly the activity drops off.

> The half-life is the time taken for the number of radioactive nuclei in an isotope to halve.

4) It is also the time taken for the activity, and so count-rate, to halve. A short half-life means the activity falls quickly, because the nuclei are very unstable and rapidly decay. Sources with a short half-life are dangerous because of the high amount of radiation they emit at the start, but they quickly become safe.

5) A long half-life means the activity falls more slowly because most of the nuclei don't decay for a long time — the source just sits there, releasing small amounts of radiation for a long time. This can be dangerous because nearby areas are exposed to radiation for (millions of) years.

One half-life

EXAMPLE: The initial activity of a sample is 640 Bq. Calculate the final activity as a percentage of the initial activity after two half-lives.

Always double check what the question is asking for — it may want a fraction, ratio or a percentage.

1) Find the activity after each half-life.

2) Now divide the final activity by the initial activity, then multiply by 100 to make it a percentage.

1 half-life: 640 ÷ 2 = 320
2 half-lives: 320 ÷ 2 = 160

(160 ÷ 640) × 100 = 0.25 × 100 = **25%**

You Can Measure Half-Life Using a Graph

1) If you plot a graph of activity against time (taking into account background radiation, p.47), it will always be shaped like the one to the right.

2) The half-life is found from the graph by finding the time interval on the bottom axis corresponding to a halving of the activity on the vertical axis. Easy.

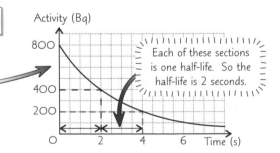

Each of these sections is one half-life. So the half-life is 2 seconds.

Activity (Bq)

The half-life of a box of chocolates is about five minutes...

Half-life — the time for the number of radioactive nuclei, the activity or the count-rate to halve. Simple.

Q1   The initial count-rate of a sample is 40 cps.
Calculate the decline in count-rate, as a ratio, after three half-lives.

[3 marks]

Background Radiation and Contamination

Forget love — <u>radiation</u> is <u>all around</u>. Don't panic too much though, it's usually a pretty <u>small amount</u>.

Background Radiation Comes From Many Sources

<u>Background radiation</u> is the <u>low-level</u> radiation that's around us <u>all the time</u>. You should always <u>measure</u> and <u>subtract</u> the background radiation from your results (to avoid systematic errors, p.5). It comes from:

1) Radioactivity of naturally occurring <u>unstable isotopes</u> which are <u>all around us</u> — in the <u>air</u>, in <u>food</u>, in <u>building materials</u> and in the <u>rocks</u> under our feet.

2) Radiation from <u>space</u>, which is known as <u>cosmic rays</u>. These come mostly from the <u>Sun</u>. Luckily, the Earth's <u>atmosphere protects</u> us from much of this radiation.

3) Radiation due to <u>human activity</u>, e.g. <u>fallout</u> from <u>nuclear explosions</u> or <u>nuclear waste</u>. But this represents a <u>tiny</u> proportion of the total background radiation.

The <u>radiation dose</u> tells you the <u>risk of harm</u> to body tissues due to exposure to radiation. It's measured in <u>sieverts</u> (Sv) (p.81). The dose from background radiation is <u>small</u>, so <u>millisieverts</u> are often used (<u>1 Sv = 1000 mSv</u>). Your radiation dose <u>varies</u> depending on <u>where you live</u> or if you have a <u>job</u> that involves <u>radiation</u>.

Coloured bits indicate more radiation from rocks

See the next page for the dangers of being exposed to radiation.

Exposure to Radiation is called Irradiation

1) Objects <u>near</u> a radioactive source are <u>irradiated</u> by it. This simply means they're <u>exposed</u> to it (we're <u>always</u> being irradiated by <u>background radiation</u> sources).

2) <u>Irradiating</u> something does <u>not</u> make it <u>radioactive</u> (and won't turn you into a superhero).

3) Keeping sources in <u>lead-lined boxes</u>, standing behind <u>barriers</u> or being in a <u>different room</u> and using <u>remote-controlled arms</u> are all ways of reducing the effects of <u>irradiation</u>.

Contamination is Radioactive Particles Getting onto Objects

1) If <u>unwanted radioactive atoms</u> get onto or into an object, the object is said to be <u>contaminated</u>. E.g. if you <u>touch</u> a radioactive source without wearing <u>gloves</u>, your hands would be <u>contaminated</u>.

2) These <u>contaminating atoms</u> might then decay, releasing <u>radiation</u> which could cause you <u>harm</u>.

3) Contamination is especially dangerous because radioactive particles could get <u>inside your body</u>.

4) <u>Gloves</u> and <u>tongs</u> should be used when handling sources, to avoid particles getting stuck to your <u>skin</u> or <u>under your nails</u>. Some industrial workers wear <u>protective suits</u> to stop them <u>breathing in</u> particles.

The Seriousness of Irradiation and Contamination Depends on the Source

<u>Contamination</u> or <u>irradiation</u> can cause different amounts of <u>harm</u> (p.48), based on the <u>radiation type</u>.

1) Outside the body, <u>beta</u> and <u>gamma</u> sources are the most dangerous. This is because <u>beta and gamma</u> can penetrate the body and get to the delicate <u>organs</u>. Alpha is less dangerous because it <u>can't penetrate the skin</u> and is easily blocked by a <u>small air gap</u> (p.44). High levels of <u>irradiation</u> from <u>all</u> sources are dangerous, but especially from ones that emit <u>beta</u> and <u>gamma</u>.

2) <u>Inside the body</u>, <u>alpha</u> sources are the most dangerous, because they do all their damage in a <u>very localised area</u>. So <u>contamination</u>, rather than irradiation, is the major concern when working with alpha sources. <u>Beta</u> sources are <u>less damaging</u> inside the body, as radiation is absorbed over a <u>wider area</u>, and some <u>passes out</u> of the body altogether. <u>Gamma</u> sources are the <u>least dangerous</u> inside the body, as they mostly <u>pass straight out</u> — they have the <u>lowest ionising power</u>, p.44.

The more we understand how radiation <u>affects our bodies</u>, the better we can <u>protect</u> ourselves when using it. This is why it's so important that research about this is published. The data is <u>peer-reviewed</u> (see p.1) and can quickly become <u>accepted</u>, leading to many <u>improvements</u> in our use of radioactive sources.

Background radiation — the ugly wallpaper of the Universe...

Make sure you can describe how to prevent irradiation and contamination, and why it's so important that you do.

Q1   Give three sources of background radiation.   [3 marks]

Uses and Risk

Radiation can be pretty useful. We use it in our homes, in industry and in medicine. But it's not without its dangers. Using radiation is all about reducing the risks whilst still keeping the benefits.

There are Risks to Using Radiation

1) Radiation can enter living cells and ionise atoms and molecules within them. This can lead to tissue damage.

2) Lower doses tend to cause minor damage without killing the cells. This can give rise to mutant cells which divide uncontrollably. This is cancer.

3) Higher doses tend to kill cells completely, causing radiation sickness (leading to vomiting, tiredness and hair loss) if a lot of cells all get blatted at once.

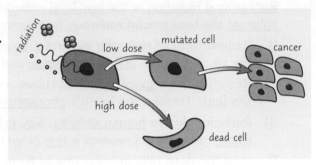

Gamma Sources are Usually Used in Medical Tracers

1) Certain radioactive isotopes can be injected into people (or they can just swallow them) and their progress around the body can be followed using an external detector. A computer converts the reading to a display showing where the strongest reading is coming from.

2) One example is the use of iodine-123, which is absorbed by the thyroid gland just like normal iodine-127, but it gives out radiation which can be detected to indicate whether the thyroid gland is taking in iodine as it should.

Iodine-123 collecting in the thyroid gland.

3) Isotopes which are taken into the body like this are usually GAMMA (never alpha), so that the radiation passes out of the body without causing much ionisation. They should have a short half-life so the radioactivity inside the patient quickly disappears.

Radiotherapy — Treating Cancer with Radiation

1) Since high doses of ionising radiation will kill all living cells, it can be used to treat cancers.

2) Gamma rays are directed carefully and at just the right dosage to kill the cancer cells without damaging too many normal cells. Radiation-emitting implants (usually beta-emitters) can also be put next to or inside tumours.

3) However, a fair bit of damage is inevitably done to normal cells, which makes the patient feel very ill. But if the cancer is successfully killed off in the end, then it's worth it.

You Have to Weigh Up the Risks and Benefits

1) For every situation, it's worth considering both the benefits and risks of using radioactive materials.

2) For example, tracers can be used to diagnose life-threatening conditions, while the risk of cancer from one use of a tracer is very small.

3) Whilst prolonged exposure to radiation poses future risks (see p.81 for comparing the risks with different medical procedures) and causes many side effects, many people with cancer choose to have radiotherapy as it may get rid of their cancer entirely. For them, the benefits outweigh the risks.

4) Perceived risk is how risky a person thinks something is. It's not the same as the actual risk of a procedure and the perceived risk can vary from person to person. See page 3 for more on this.

Revision sickness — well yes, it does all get a bit tedious...

It may seem odd to use radiation in medicine, but there you go. Make sure you can explain that using any kind of radiation has risks, but that the benefits are often large enough that the risks are considered worth it.

Q1   Describe how radiotherapy is used to treat cancerous tumours.   [2 marks]

Q2   a) Describe how gamma emitters are used as medical tracers.   [2 marks]
       b) Explain why some patients might not want to be diagnosed using a medical tracer.   [2 marks]

Fission and Fusion

Splitting up or squishing together atoms releases lots of useful energy, but it can have explosive consequences.

Nuclear Fission — Splitting a Large, Unstable Nucleus

Nuclear fission is a type of nuclear reaction that is used to release energy from large and unstable atoms (e.g. uranium or plutonium) by splitting them into smaller atoms.

1) Spontaneous (unforced) fission rarely happens.
   Usually, the nucleus has to absorb a neutron before it will split.

2) When the atom splits it forms two new lighter elements that are roughly the same size (and that have some energy in their kinetic energy stores).

3) Two or three neutrons are also released when an atom splits. If any of these neutrons are moving slow enough to be absorbed by another nucleus, they can cause more fission to occur. This is a chain reaction.

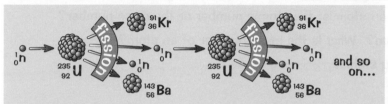

> You may have to draw or complete a diagram to show a chain reaction in the exam, so make sure you're happy with fission reactions.

4) The energy not transferred to the kinetic energy stores of the products is carried away by gamma rays.

5) The energy carried away by the gamma rays, and in the kinetic energy stores of the remaining free neutrons and the other decay products, can be used to heat water, making steam to turn turbines and generators (p.97).

6) The amount of energy produced by fission in a nuclear reactor is controlled by changing how quickly the chain reaction can occur. This is done using control rods, which are lowered and raised inside a nuclear reactor to absorb neutrons, slow down the chain reaction and control the amount of energy released.

7) Uncontrolled chain reactions quickly lead to lots of energy being released as an explosion — this is how nuclear weapons work.

Nuclear Fusion — Joining Small Nuclei

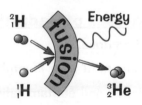

1) Nuclear fusion is the opposite of nuclear fission.

2) In nuclear fusion, two light nuclei collide at high speed and join (fuse) to create a larger, heavier nucleus. For example, hydrogen nuclei can fuse to produce a helium nucleus.

3) The heavier nucleus produced by fusion does not have as much mass as the two separate, light nuclei did. Some of the mass of the lighter nuclei is converted to energy (don't panic, you don't need to know how). This energy is then released as radiation.

4) Fusion releases a lot of energy (more than fission for a given mass of fuel).

5) So far, scientists haven't found a way of using fusion to generate energy for us to use. The temperatures and pressures needed for fusion are so high that fusion reactors are really hard and expensive to build.

Pity they can't release energy by confusion...*

Thankfully you don't need to know the complicated processes behind fission and fusion, you just need to have an idea of the steps in them. Remember that fission rarely occurs spontaneously, it often needs a prod to get it going.

Q1 a) Explain what happens during a forced fission reaction.   [4 marks]
    b) Draw a diagram showing how fission can lead to a chain reaction.   [3 marks]

*There'd be plenty of physics books to use as fuel.

Revision Questions for Topic 4

Well, that's the end of Topic 4 — hopefully it wasn't too painful. Time to see how much you've absorbed.

- Try these questions and tick off each one when you get it right.
- When you've done all the questions under a heading and are completely happy with it, tick it off.

The Atomic Model (p.43) ☑

1) Briefly explain how the model of an atom has changed over time. ☑
2) What happens to an electron in an atom if it releases EM radiation? ☑
3) Who provided evidence to suggest the existence of the neutron? ☑
4) True or false? Atoms have no overall charge. ☑
5) What happens to an atom if it loses one or more of its electrons? ☑

Nuclear Decay and Half-life (p.44-46) ☑

6) Which number defines what element an atom is: the atomic number or the mass number? ☑
7) What is the atomic number of an atom? What is the mass number of an atom? ☑
8) What is an isotope? Are they usually stable? ☑
9) What is radioactive decay? ☑
10) Name four things that may be emitted during radioactive decay. ☑
11) For the three types of ionising radiation, give: a) their ionising power, b) their range in air. ☑
12) Explain why alpha radiation could not be used to check the thickness of metal sheets. ☑
13) Draw the symbols for both alpha and beta radiation in nuclear equations. ☑
14) What type of nuclear decay doesn't change the mass or charge of the nucleus? ☑
15) What is the activity of a source? What are its units? ☑
16) Define half-life. ☑
17) True or false? A short half-life means a small proportion of atoms are decaying per second. ☑
18) Explain the dangers of a radioactive source with a long half-life. ☑
19) Explain how you would find the half-life of a source, given a graph of its activity over time. ☑

Dangers and Uses of Radiation (p.47-48) ☑

20) Define radiation dose. ☑
21) State two aspects of your lifestyle that can affect your radiation dose. ☑
22) Define irradiation and contamination. ☑
23) Compare the hazards of being irradiated and contaminated by:
      a) an alpha source, b) a gamma source. ☑
24) Give two examples of how to protect against: a) contamination, b) irradiation. ☑
25) Describe some of the risks involved with using radiation. ☑
26) Give two ways that radiation is used in medicine. ☑

Fission and Fusion (p.49) ☑

27) Define fission and fusion. ☑
28) True or false? Fission is usually spontaneous. ☑
29) Describe what a chain reaction is, and what happens when it is uncontrolled. ☑
30) Explain the difference between fission and fusion. ☑

Contact and Non-Contact Forces

When you're talking about the <u>forces</u> acting on an object, it's not enough to just talk about the <u>size</u> of each force. You need to know their <u>direction</u> too — force is a <u>vector</u>, with a size and a direction.

Vectors Have Magnitude and Direction

1) Force is a <u>vector quantity</u> — vector quantities have a <u>magnitude</u> and a <u>direction</u>.

2) Lots of <u>physical quantities</u> are vector quantities:

   <u>Vector quantities</u>: force, velocity, displacement, acceleration, momentum, etc.

3) Some physical quantities <u>only</u> have magnitude and <u>no direction</u>. These are called <u>scalar quantities</u>:

   <u>Scalar quantities</u>: speed, distance, mass, temperature, time, etc.

4) Vectors are usually represented by an <u>arrow</u> — the <u>length</u> of the arrow shows the <u>magnitude</u>, and the <u>direction</u> of the arrow shows the <u>direction of the quantity</u>.

> <u>Velocity</u> is a <u>vector</u>, but <u>speed</u> is a <u>scalar</u> quantity.
>
> Both bikes are travelling at the same <u>speed</u>, v (the <u>length</u> of each arrow is the same).
>
> They have <u>different velocities</u> because they are travelling in different <u>directions</u>.

Forces Can be Contact or Non-Contact

1) A <u>force</u> is a <u>push</u> or a <u>pull</u> on an object that is caused by it <u>interacting</u> with something.

2) All forces are either <u>contact</u> or <u>non-contact</u> forces.

3) When <u>two objects</u> have to be <u>touching</u> for a force to act, that force is called a <u>contact force</u>.

   E.g. friction, air resistance, tension in ropes, normal contact force, etc.

4) If the objects <u>do not need to be touching</u> for the force to act, the force is a <u>non-contact force</u>.

   E.g. magnetic force, gravitational force, electrostatic force, etc.

5) When two objects <u>interact</u>, there is a <u>force</u> produced on <u>both</u> objects.
   An <u>interaction pair</u> is a pair of forces that are <u>equal</u> and <u>opposite</u> and act on two <u>interacting</u> objects. (This is basically Newton's Third Law — see p.65.)

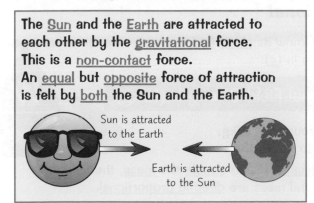

The <u>Sun</u> and the <u>Earth</u> are attracted to each other by the <u>gravitational</u> force. This is a <u>non-contact</u> force. An <u>equal</u> but <u>opposite</u> force of attraction is felt by <u>both</u> the Sun and the Earth.

Sun is attracted to the Earth

Earth is attracted to the Sun

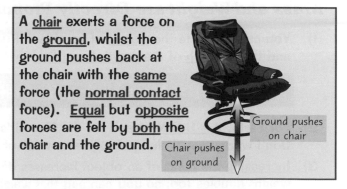

A <u>chair</u> exerts a force on the <u>ground</u>, whilst the ground pushes back at the chair with the <u>same</u> force (the <u>normal contact</u> force). <u>Equal</u> but <u>opposite</u> forces are felt by <u>both</u> the chair and the ground.

Ground pushes on chair

Chair pushes on ground

My life's feeling pretty scalar — I've no idea where I'm headed...

This all seems pretty basic, but it's vital you understand it if you want to make it through the rest of this topic.

Q1   A tennis ball is dropped from a height. Name one contact force and one non-contact force that act on the ball as it falls.   [2 marks]

Q2   Name two examples of: a) a scalar quantity   b) a vector quantity   [4 marks]

Weight, Mass and Gravity

Now for something a bit more __attractive__ — the force of __gravity__. Enjoy...

Gravitational Force is the Force of Attraction Between Masses

__Gravity__ attracts __all__ masses, but you only notice it when one of the masses is __really really big__, e.g. a planet.
Anything near a planet or star is __attracted__ to it __very strongly__.

This has __two__ important effects:

1) On the surface of a planet, it makes all things
    fall towards the __ground__.

2) It gives everything a __weight__.

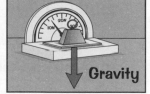

Gravity

Weight and Mass are Not the Same

1) __Mass__ is just the __amount of 'stuff'__ in an object. For any given
    object this will have the same value __anywhere__ in the universe.

2) __Weight__ is the __force__ acting on an object due to __gravity__ (the __pull__ of the __gravitational force__ on the object).
    Close to Earth, this __force__ is caused by the __gravitational field__ around the Earth.

3) Gravitational field __strength__ varies with __location__. It's __stronger__ the __closer__ you
    are to the mass causing the field, and stronger for __larger__ masses.

4) The __weight__ of an object depends on the __strength__ of the __gravitational field__ at the __location__ of
    the object. This means that the weight of an object __changes__ with its location.

5) For example, an object has the __same__ mass whether it's on __Earth__ or on the __Moon__ — but its __weight__
    will be __different__. A 1 kg mass will __weigh less__ on the Moon (about 1.6 N) than it does on Earth
    (about 9.8 N), simply because the __gravitational field strength__ on the surface of the Moon is __less__.

6) Weight is a __force__ measured in __newtons__. You can think of the force as acting
    from a __single point__ on the object, called its __centre of mass__
    (a point at which you assume the __whole__ mass is concentrated).
    For a __uniform object__ (one that's the same density, p.38, throughout
    and is a regular shape), this will be at the __centre__ of the object.

7) Weight is measured using a calibrated __spring__ balance (or __newtonmeter__).

8) __Mass__ is __not__ a force. It's measured in __kilograms__ with a __mass__ balance
    (an old-fashioned pair of balancing scales).

centre of mass

weight

Mass and Weight are Directly Proportional

1) You can calculate the __weight__ of an object if you know its __mass__ (m)
    and the __strength__ of the __gravitational field__ that it is in (g):

Weight (N) = Mass (kg) × Gravitational Field Strength (N/kg)

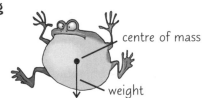

$$\frac{W}{m \times g}$$

2) For Earth, $g \approx 9.8$ N/kg and for the Moon it's around 1.6 N/kg.
    Don't worry, you'll always be given a value of g to use in the exam.

3) __Increasing__ the __mass__ of an object increases its __weight__. If you __double__ the __mass__, the
    weight __doubles__ too, so you can say that weight and mass are __directly proportional__.

4) You can write this, using the __direct proportionality symbol__, as $W \propto m$.

I don't think you understand the gravity of this situation...

Remember that weight is a force due to gravity that acts from an object's centre of mass. It changes depending on
the strength of the gravitational field the object is in (and is directly proportional to the mass of the object too).

Q1   Calculate the weight in newtons of a 5 kg mass:

     a) on Earth ($g \approx 9.8$ N/kg)   b) on the Moon ($g \approx 1.6$ N/kg)   [4 marks]

Resultant Forces and Work Done

I'm sure you're no stranger to <u>doing work</u>, but in physics it's all to do with <u>overall forces</u> and <u>energy</u>.

Free Body Diagrams Show All the Forces Acting on an Object

1) You need to be able to <u>describe</u> all the <u>forces</u> acting on an <u>isolated object</u> or a <u>system</u> (p.11) — i.e. <u>every</u> force <u>acting on</u> the object or system but <u>none</u> of the forces the object or system <u>exerts</u> on the rest of the world.

2) For example, a skydiver's <u>weight</u> acts on him pulling him towards the ground and <u>drag</u> (air resistance) also acts on him, in the <u>opposite direction</u> to his motion.

3) This can be shown using a <u>free body diagram</u> like the one on the right.

4) The <u>sizes</u> of the arrows show the <u>relative magnitudes</u> of the forces and the <u>directions</u> show the directions of the forces acting on the object.

A Resultant Force is the Overall Force on a Point or Object

1) In most <u>real</u> situations there are at least <u>two forces</u> acting on an object along any direction.

2) If you have a <u>number of forces</u> acting at a single point, you can replace them with a <u>single force</u> (so long as the single force has the <u>same effect</u> as all the original forces together).

3) This single force is called the <u>resultant force</u>. (There's a <u>downward resultant force</u> acting on the <u>skydiver</u> above.)

4) If the forces all act along the <u>same line</u> (they're all parallel), the <u>overall effect</u> is found by <u>adding</u> those going in the <u>same</u> direction and <u>subtracting</u> any going in the opposite direction.

EXAMPLE: For the following free body diagram, calculate the resultant force acting on the van.

1) Consider the <u>horizontal</u> and <u>vertical</u> directions <u>separately</u>.

2) State the <u>size</u> and <u>direction</u> of the <u>resultant</u> force.

Vertical: 1500 − 1500 = 0 N

Horizontal: 1200 − 1000 N = 200 N

The resultant force is 200 N to the left.

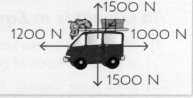

If A Resultant Force Moves An Object, Work is Done

> When a <u>force</u> moves an object through a <u>distance</u>, **ENERGY IS TRANSFERRED** and **WORK IS DONE** on the object.

1) To make something <u>move</u> (or <u>keep</u> it moving if there are <u>frictional forces</u>), a <u>force</u> must be applied.

2) The thing <u>applying the force</u> needs a <u>source</u> of <u>energy</u> (like <u>fuel</u> or <u>food</u>).

3) The force does '<u>work</u>' to <u>move</u> the object and <u>energy</u> is <u>transferred</u> from one <u>store</u> to another (p.11).

4) Whether energy is transferred '<u>usefully</u>' (e.g. <u>lifting a load</u>) or is '<u>wasted</u>' (p.14) you can still say that '<u>work is done</u>'. Just like Batman and Bruce Wayne, '<u>work done</u>' and '<u>energy transferred</u>' are the same.

> When you push something along a <u>rough surface</u> (like a <u>carpet</u>) you are doing work <u>against frictional forces</u>. Energy is being <u>transferred</u> to the <u>kinetic energy store</u> of the <u>object</u> because it starts <u>moving</u>, but some is also being transferred to <u>thermal energy stores</u> due to the friction. This causes the overall <u>temperature</u> of the object to <u>increase</u>. (Like <u>rubbing your hands together</u> to warm them up.)

5) You can find out <u>how much</u> work has been done using:

6) <u>One joule of work</u> is done when a <u>force of one newton</u> causes an object to move a <u>distance of one metre</u>. You need to be able to <u>convert</u> joules to newton metres: <u>1 J = 1 Nm</u>.

$$W = Fs$$

Force (N)

Work done (J)

Distance (moved along the line of action of the force) (m)

Consolidate all your forces into one easy-to-manage force...

Free body diagrams make most force questions easier, so start by sketching one. Then get to work.

Q1 A force of 20 N pushes an object 20 cm. Calculate the work done on the object. [3 marks]

Calculating Forces

Scale drawings are useful things — they can help you resolve forces or work out the resultant force.

Use Scale Drawings to Find Resultant Forces

1) Draw all the forces acting on an object, to scale, 'tip-to-tail'.

2) Then draw a straight line from the start of the first force to the end of the last force — this is the resultant force.

3) Measure the length of the resultant force on the diagram to find the magnitude and the angle to find the direction of the force.

EXAMPLE: A man is on an electric bicycle that has a driving force of 4 N north. However, the wind produces a force of 3 N east. Find the magnitude and direction of the resultant force.

1) Start by drawing a scale drawing of the forces acting.

2) Make sure you choose a sensible scale (e.g. 1 cm = 1 N).

3) Draw the resultant from the tail of the first arrow to the tip of the last arrow.

4) Measure the length of the resultant with a ruler and use the scale to find the force in N.

5) Use a protractor to measure the direction as a bearing.

A bearing is an angle measured clockwise from north, given as a 3 digit number, e.g. 10° = 010°.

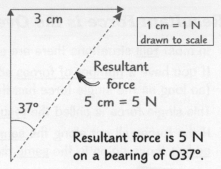

3 cm

1 cm = 1 N drawn to scale

4 cm

Resultant force
5 cm = 5 N

37°

Resultant force is 5 N on a bearing of 037°.

An Object is in Equilibrium if the Forces on it are Balanced

1) If all of the forces acting on an object combine to give a resultant force of zero, the object is in equilibrium.

2) On a scale diagram, this means that the tip of the last force you draw should end where the tail of the first force you drew begins. E.g. for three forces, the scale diagram will form a triangle.

3) You might be given forces acting on an object and told to find a missing force, given that the object is in equilibrium. To do this, draw out the forces you do know (to scale and tip-to-tail), join the end of the last force to the start of the first force. This line is the missing force so you can measure its size and direction.

Make sure you draw the last force in the right direction. It's in the opposite direction to how you'd draw a resultant force.

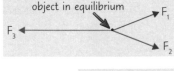

object in equilibrium

F_1

F_3

F_2

Tip-to-tail the forces join up...

F_1 F_2

F_3

...so the resultant force is zero.

You Can Split a Force into Components

1) Not all forces act horizontally or vertically — some act at awkward angles.

2) To make these easier to deal with, they can be split into two components at right angles to each other (usually horizontal and vertical).

3) Acting together, these components have the same effect as the single force.

4) You can resolve a force (split it into components) by drawing it on a scale grid. Draw the force to scale, and then add the horizontal and vertical components along the grid lines. Then you can just measure them.

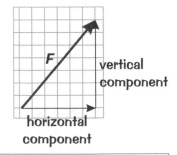

F

vertical component

horizontal component

Don't blow things out of proportion — it's only scale drawings...

Keep those pencils sharp and those scale drawings accurate — or you'll end up with the wrong answer.

Q1   A toy boat crosses a stream. The motor provides a 12 N driving force to the north. The river's current causes a force of 5 N west to act on the boat. Find the magnitude of the resultant force. [2 marks]

Forces and Elasticity

You can use forces to stretch things too. The fun never ends...

Stretching, Compressing or Bending Transfers Energy

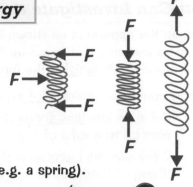

1) When you apply a force to an object you may cause it to stretch, compress or bend.

2) To do this, you need more than one force acting on the object (otherwise the object would simply move in the direction of the applied force, instead of changing shape).

3) An object has been elastically deformed if it can go back to its original shape and length after the force has been removed.

4) Objects that can be elastically deformed are called elastic objects (e.g. a spring).

5) An object has been inelastically deformed if it doesn't return to its original shape and length after the force has been removed.

6) Work is done when a force stretches or compresses an object and causes energy to be transferred to the elastic potential energy store of the object. If it is elastically deformed, ALL this energy is transferred to the object's elastic potential energy store (see p.12).

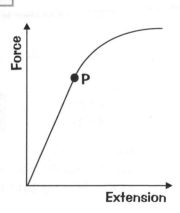

Elastic objects — useful for passing exams and scaring small children

Extension is Directly Proportional to Force...

If a spring is supported at the top and then a weight is attached to the bottom, it stretches.

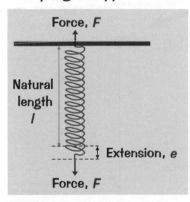

1) The extension of a stretched spring (or other elastic object) is directly proportional to the load or force applied — so $F \propto e$.

2) This is the equation:

$$F = ke$$

Force (N) — Spring constant (N/m) — Extension (m)

3) The spring constant depends on the material that you are stretching — a stiffer spring has a greater spring constant.

4) The equation also works for compression (where e is just the difference between the natural and compressed lengths — the compression).

...but this Stops Working when the Force is Great Enough

There's a limit to the amount of force you can apply to an object for the extension to keep on increasing proportionally.

1) The graph shows force against extension for an elastic object.

2) There is a maximum force above which the graph curves, showing that extension is no longer proportional to force. This is known as the limit of proportionality and is shown on the graph at the point marked P.

3) You might see graphs with these axes the other way around — extension-force graphs. The graph still starts has a straight part, but starts to curve upwards once you go past the limit of proportionality, instead of downwards.

I could make a joke, but I don't want to stretch myself...

That equation is pretty simple, but that doesn't mean you can skip over it. Have a go at the question below.

Q1 A spring is fixed at one end and a force of 1 N is applied to the other end, causing it to stretch. The spring extends by 2 cm. Calculate the spring constant of the spring. [4 marks]

Investigating Springs

You can do an easy <u>experiment</u> to see exactly how adding <u>masses</u> to a spring causes it to <u>stretch</u>.

You Can Investigate the Link Between Force and Extension

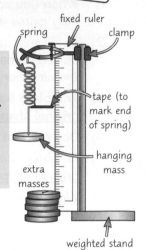

fixed ruler

spring

clamp

tape (to mark end of spring)

hanging mass

extra masses

weighted stand

Set up the apparatus as shown in the diagram. Make sure you have plenty of extra masses, then measure the <u>mass</u> of each (with a mass balance) and calculate its <u>weight</u> (the <u>force</u> applied) using $W = mg$ (p.52).

You could do a quick <u>pilot experiment</u> first to check your masses are a good size:

- Using an <u>identical spring</u> to the one you'll be testing, <u>load</u> it with <u>masses</u> one at a time up to a total of <u>five</u>. Measure the <u>extension each time</u> you add another mass.
- Work out the <u>increase</u> in the extension of the spring for <u>each</u> of your masses. If any of them cause a <u>bigger increase</u> than the previous masses, you've gone past the spring's <u>limit of proportionality</u>. If this happens, you'll need to use <u>smaller masses</u>, or else you won't get enough measurements for your graph.

1) Measure the <u>natural length</u> of the spring (when <u>no load</u> is applied) with a <u>millimetre ruler</u> clamped to the stand. Make sure you take the reading at eye level and add a <u>marker</u> (e.g. a thin strip of tape) to the <u>bottom</u> of the spring to make the reading more accurate.

2) Add a mass to the spring and allow it to come to <u>rest</u>. Record the mass and measure the new <u>length</u> of the spring. The <u>extension</u> is the change in length.

3) <u>Repeat</u> this process until you have enough measurements (no fewer than 6).

4) <u>Plot</u> a <u>force-extension graph</u> of your results. It will only start to <u>curve</u> if you <u>exceed</u> the <u>limit of proportionality</u>, but don't worry if yours doesn't (as long as you've got the straight line bit).

To check whether the deformation is elastic or inelastic, you can remove each mass temporarily and check the spring goes back to the previous extension.

- When the line of best fit is a <u>straight line</u> it means there is a <u>linear</u> relationship between force and extension (they're <u>directly proportional</u>, see previous page). $F = ke$, so the <u>gradient</u> of the straight line is equal to k, the <u>spring constant</u>.

- When the line begins to <u>bend</u>, the relationship is now <u>non-linear</u> between force and extension — the spring <u>stretches more</u> for each unit increase in force.

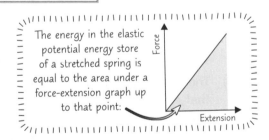

Force (N)

Extension (m)

You Can Work Out Energy Stored for Linear Relationships

1) As long as a spring is not stretched <u>past</u> its <u>limit of proportionality</u>, the <u>work done</u> in stretching (or compressing) a spring can be found using:

Elastic potential energy (J)

$$E_e = \frac{1}{2}ke^2$$

Spring constant (N/m)

Extension (m)

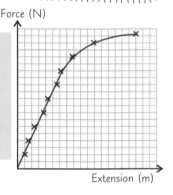

The energy in the elastic potential energy store of a stretched spring is equal to the area under a force-extension graph up to that point:

Force

Extension

2) For <u>elastic deformation</u>, this formula can be used to calculate the <u>energy stored</u> in a spring's elastic potential energy store. It's also the energy <u>transferred to</u> the spring as it's <u>deformed</u> (or <u>transferred by</u> the spring as it returns to its <u>original shape</u>).

Time to spring into action and learn all this...

Remember that you can only use the gradient to find the spring constant if the graph is linear (a straight line).

Q1 A spring with a spring constant of 40 N/m extends elastically by 2.5 cm. Calculate the amount of energy stored in its elastic potential energy store. [3 marks]

Moments

Once you can calculate <u>moments</u>, you can work out if a seesaw is <u>balanced</u>. Useful thing, physics.

A Moment is the Turning Effect of a Force

A force, or several forces, can cause an object to <u>rotate</u>. The <u>turning effect</u> of a force is called its <u>moment</u>. The <u>size</u> of the <u>moment</u> of the force is given by:

Moment of a force (Nm) — $M = Fd$ — Force (N)

Distance (m) — the perpendicular distance from the pivot to the line of action of the force

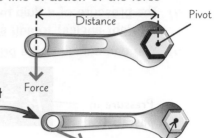

1) The <u>force</u> on the spanner causes a <u>turning effect</u> or <u>moment</u> on the nut (which acts as pivot). A <u>larger</u> force or a <u>longer</u> distance (spanner) would mean a <u>larger</u> moment.

2) To get the <u>maximum</u> moment (or turning effect) you need to push at <u>right angles</u> (<u>perpendicular</u>) to the spanner. Pushing at <u>any other angle</u> means a <u>smaller distance</u>, and so a <u>smaller moment</u>.

If the total <u>anticlockwise moment</u> equals the total <u>clockwise moment</u> about a pivot, the object is <u>balanced</u> and <u>won't turn</u>. You can use the equation above to find a <u>missing force</u> or <u>distance</u> in these situations.

EXAMPLE: A 6 m long steel girder weighing 1000 N rests horizontally on a pole 1 m from one end. What is the tension in a supporting cable attached vertically to the other end?

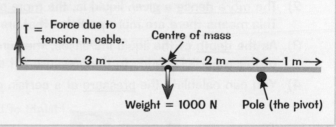

1) For the girder to balance, the <u>total anticlockwise</u> moment should <u>equal</u> the <u>total clockwise</u> moment.

$$1000 \times 2 = 5 \times T$$

2) Stick in the numbers you know and <u>rearrange for T</u>.

$$T = 2000 \div 5 = 400 \text{ N}$$

Levers Make it Easier for us to Do Work

Levers <u>increase</u> the <u>distance</u> from the pivot at which the <u>force</u> is applied. Since $M = Fd$ this means <u>less force</u> is needed to get the <u>same moment</u>.

This means levers make it <u>easier</u> to do <u>work</u>, e.g. <u>lift a load</u> or <u>turn a nut</u>.

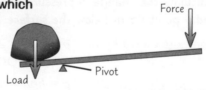

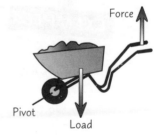

Gears Transmit Rotational Effects

1) <u>Gears</u> are circular discs with '<u>teeth</u>' around their edges.

2) Their teeth <u>interlock</u> so that <u>turning</u> one causes <u>another</u> to turn, in the <u>opposite</u> direction.

3) They are used to <u>transmit</u> the <u>rotational effect</u> of a <u>force</u> from one place to another.

4) <u>Different sized</u> gears can be used to <u>change</u> the <u>moment</u> of the force. A force transmitted to a <u>larger</u> gear will cause a <u>bigger</u> moment, as the <u>distance</u> to the pivot is greater.

5) The <u>larger gear</u> will <u>turn slower</u> than the smaller gear.

Don't get in a spin — gear up for some more physics...

Moments can be used in lots of different situations, so get your head around them sooner rather than later.

Q1 Your brother weighs 300 N and sits 2 m from the pivot of a seesaw. If you weigh 600 N, what distance from the pivot, on the other side of the seesaw, should you sit to balance it? [3 marks]

Fluid Pressure

Hopefully reading this page will make you feel a little less pressured about your physics exam.

Pressure is the Force per Unit Area

1) <u>Fluids</u> are substances that can '<u>flow</u>' because their particles are able to <u>move around</u>.
2) As these particles move around, they <u>collide</u> with surfaces and <u>other particles</u>.
3) Particles are light, but they still have a <u>mass</u> and exert a <u>force</u> on the object they collide with. <u>Pressure</u> is <u>force per unit area</u>, so this means the particles exert a <u>pressure</u>.
4) The <u>pressure</u> of a fluid means a <u>force</u> is exerted <u>normal</u> (at <u>right angles</u>) to any <u>surface</u> in contact with the fluid.
5) You can calculate the <u>pressure</u> at the <u>surface</u> of a fluid by using:

A fluid is either a liquid or a gas.

$$p = \frac{F}{A}$$

Pressure in pascals (Pa)
Force normal to a surface (N)
Area of that surface (m²)

Pressure in a Liquid Depends on Depth and Density

1) <u>Density</u> is a measure of the '<u>compactness</u>' of a substance, i.e. how <u>close together</u> the particles in a substance are (p.38). For a given <u>liquid</u>, the <u>density</u> is <u>uniform</u> (the <u>same everywhere</u>) and it <u>doesn't vary</u> with <u>shape</u> or <u>size</u>. The density of a <u>gas</u> can vary though (see next page).
2) The <u>more dense</u> a given liquid is, the <u>more particles</u> it has in a certain space. This means there are more particles that are able to <u>collide</u> so the <u>pressure is higher</u>.
3) As the <u>depth</u> of the liquid increases, the number of particles <u>above</u> that point increases. The weight of these particles adds to the pressure felt at that point, so liquid pressure increases with depth.
4) You can calculate the <u>pressure</u> at a certain <u>depth</u> due to the <u>column</u> of liquid <u>above</u> using:

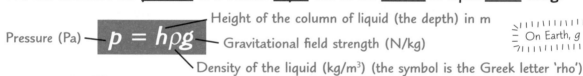

Pressure (Pa) — $p = h\rho g$
Height of the column of liquid (the depth) in m
Gravitational field strength (N/kg)
Density of the liquid (kg/m³) (the symbol is the Greek letter 'rho')

On Earth, g = 9.8 N/kg.

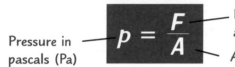 **EXAMPLE:** Calculate the change in pressure between a point 25 m below the surface of water and a point 45 m below the surface. The density of water is 1000 kg/m³.

1) Calculate the <u>pressure</u> caused by the water at a depth of <u>25 m</u>.

$p = h\rho g = 25 \times 1000 \times 9.8$
$= 245\ 000$ Pa

2) Do the same for a depth of <u>45 m</u>.

$p = h\rho g = 45 \times 1000 \times 9.8$
$= 441\ 000$ Pa

3) <u>Take away</u> the pressure at <u>25 m</u> from the pressure at <u>45 m</u>.

$441\ 000 - 245\ 000 = 196\ 000$ Pa (or 196 kPa)

Check your answer makes sense (you can't get negative pressure).

You could write the answer above in <u>standard form</u> — it's a way of writing <u>very big</u> or <u>very small</u> numbers. Numbers in standard form always look like this:

A is always a number between 1 and 10.

$$A \times 10^n$$

n is the number of places the decimal point would move if you wrote the number out fully. It's negative for numbers less than 1, and positive for numbers greater than 1.

So 200 000 Pa would be written as 2×10^5 Pa in standard form.

So a gas is a fluid — next they'll be telling me custard is a solid...

Pressure = force ÷ area doesn't just apply to fluids — it's true for any situation a force acts on an area

Q1 Calculate the force exerted on a 10 m² area by a pressure of 200 kPa. [3 marks]

Q2 At a point 5.0 cm below the surface of a jug of olive oil, the pressure due to the oil is 450 Pa. Calculate the density of olive oil. The gravitational field strength of Earth is 9.8 N/kg. [3 marks]

Upthrust and Atmospheric Pressure

Fluid pressure can explain why potatoes sink and apples float. Because you've been dying to know...

Objects in Fluids Experience Upthrust

Pressure

Pineapple displaces this much water.

Pressure

Upthrust is equal to the weight of this amount of water.

1) When an object is submerged in a fluid (either partially or completely), the pressure of the fluid exerts a force on it from every direction.

2) Pressure increases with depth, so the force exerted on the bottom of the object is larger than the force acting on the top of the object.

3) This causes a resultant force (p.53) upwards, known as upthrust.

4) The upthrust is equal to the weight of fluid that has been displaced (pushed out of the way) by the object. E.g. the upthrust on a pineapple in water is equal to the weight of a pineapple-shaped volume of water.

An Object Floats if its Weight = Upthrust

1) If the upthrust on an object is equal to the object's weight, then the forces balance and the object floats.

2) If an object's weight is more than the upthrust, the object sinks.

3) Whether or not an object will float depends on its density.

4) An object that is less dense than the fluid it is placed in weighs less than the equivalent volume of fluid. This means it displaces a volume of fluid that is equal to its weight before it is completely submerged.

5) At this point, the object's weight is equal to the upthrust, so the object floats.

6) An object that is denser than the fluid it is placed in is unable to displace enough fluid to equal its weight. This means that its weight is always larger than the upthrust, so it sinks.

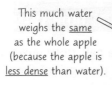

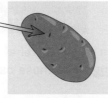

This much water weighs the same as the whole apple (because the apple is less dense than water).

The apple has displaced a volume of water equal to its weight so it floats.

This much water weighs less than a potato (because the potato is denser than water).

The potato can never displace a volume of water equal to its weight so it sinks.

Submarines make use of upthrust. To sink, large tanks are filled with water to increase the weight of the submarine so that it is more than the upthrust. To rise to the surface, the tanks are filled with compressed air to reduce the weight so that it's less than the upthrust.

Atmospheric Pressure Decreases with Height

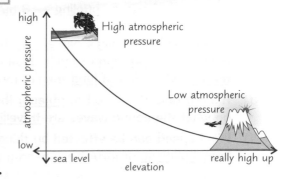

high

atmospheric pressure

low

sea level · elevation · really high up

High atmospheric pressure

Low atmospheric pressure

1) The atmosphere is a layer of air that surrounds Earth. It is thin compared to the size of the Earth.

2) Atmospheric pressure is created on a surface by air molecules colliding with the surface.

3) As the altitude (height above Earth) increases, atmospheric pressure decreases.

4) This is because as the altitude increases, the atmosphere gets less dense, so there are fewer air molecules that are able to collide with the surface.

5) There are also fewer air molecules above a surface as the height increases. This means that the weight of the air above it, which contributes to atmospheric pressure, decreases with altitude.

Next time you're feeling pressured go on a hike...

Atmospheric pressure and liquid pressure are similar — but the density of the atmosphere changes (unlike liquids).

Q1   Explain why a wooden object ($\rho = 700$ kg/m³) floats in water ($\rho = 1000$ kg/m³).   [3 marks]

Distance, Displacement, Speed and Velocity

Time for a quick recap on <u>distance</u> and <u>speed</u>. You should race through this page. On your marks...

Distance is Scalar, Displacement is a Vector

1) <u>Distance</u> is just <u>how far</u> an object has moved. It's a <u>scalar</u> quantity (p.51) so it doesn't involve <u>direction</u>.

2) Displacement is a <u>vector</u> quantity. It measures the distance and direction in a <u>straight line</u> from an object's <u>starting point</u> to its <u>finishing point</u> — e.g. the plane flew 5 metres <u>north</u>. The direction could be <u>relative to a point</u>, e.g. <u>towards the school</u>, or a <u>bearing</u> (a <u>three-digit angle from north</u>, e.g. <u>035°</u>).

3) If you walk 5 m <u>north</u>, then 5 m <u>south</u>, your <u>displacement</u> is <u>0 m</u> but the <u>distance</u> travelled is <u>10 m</u>.

Speed and Velocity are Both How Fast You're Going

1) <u>Speed and velocity</u> both measure <u>how fast</u> you're going, but <u>speed</u> is a <u>scalar</u> and <u>velocity</u> is a <u>vector</u>:

> <u>Speed</u> is just <u>how fast</u> you're going (e.g. 30 mph or 20 m/s) with no regard to the direction. <u>Velocity</u> is speed in a given <u>direction</u>, e.g. 30 mph north or 20 m/s, 060°.

2) This means you can have objects travelling at a <u>constant speed</u> with a <u>changing velocity</u>. This happens when the object is <u>changing direction</u> whilst staying at the <u>same speed</u>. An object moving in a <u>circle</u> at a <u>constant speed</u> has a <u>constantly changing</u> velocity, as the direction is <u>always changing</u> (e.g. a <u>car</u> going around a <u>roundabout</u>).

3) If you want to <u>measure</u> the <u>speed</u> of an object that's moving with a <u>constant speed</u>, you should <u>time</u> how long it takes the object to travel a certain <u>distance</u>, e.g. using a <u>ruler</u> and a <u>stopwatch</u>. You can then <u>calculate</u> the object's <u>speed</u> from your measurements using this <u>formula</u>:

$$s = vt$$

distance travelled (m) = speed (m/s) × time (s)

4) Objects <u>rarely</u> travel at a <u>constant speed</u>. E.g. when you <u>walk</u>, <u>run</u> or travel in a <u>car</u>, your speed is <u>always</u> <u>changing</u>. For these cases, the formula above gives the <u>average</u> (<u>mean</u>) speed during that time.

You Need to Know Some Typical Everyday Speeds

1) Whilst every person, train, car etc. is <u>different</u>, there is usually a <u>typical speed</u> that each object travels at. <u>Remember</u> these typical speeds for everyday objects:

A person <u>walking</u> — <u>1.5 m/s</u>	A <u>car</u> — <u>25 m/s</u>
A person <u>running</u> — <u>3 m/s</u>	A <u>train</u> — <u>55 m/s</u>
A person <u>cycling</u> — <u>6 m/s</u>	A <u>plane</u> — <u>250 m/s</u>

2) Lots of different things can <u>affect</u> the speed something travels at. For example, the speed at which a person can <u>walk</u>, <u>run</u> or <u>cycle</u> depends on their <u>fitness</u>, their <u>age</u>, the <u>distance travelled</u> and the <u>terrain</u> (what kind of <u>land</u> they're moving over, e.g. roads, fields) as well as many other factors.

3) It's not only the speed of <u>objects</u> that varies. The speed of <u>sound</u> (<u>330 m/s</u> in <u>air</u>) <u>changes</u> depending on what the sound waves are <u>travelling</u> through, and the <u>speed of wind</u> is affected by many factors.

4) Wind speed can be affected by things like <u>temperature</u>, atmospheric <u>pressure</u> and if there are any large <u>buildings</u> or structures nearby (e.g. forests reduce the speed of the air travelling through them).

Ah, speed equals distance over time — that old chestnut...

Remember those typical speeds of objects — you might need to use them to make estimates.

Q1 A sprinter runs 200 m in 25 s. Calculate his speed. [3 marks]

Q2 Marie walks her dog after school. She takes a route of 1500 m that starts at and returns to her house.
State: a) the distance she travels b) her displacement [2 marks]

Acceleration

Uniform acceleration sounds fancy, but it's just speeding up (or slowing down) at a constant rate.

Acceleration is How Quickly You're Speeding Up

1) Acceleration is definitely not the same as velocity or speed.
2) Acceleration is the change in velocity in a certain amount of time.
3) You can find the average acceleration of an object using:

Acceleration (m/s²)————$a = \dfrac{\Delta v}{t}$————Change in velocity (m/s)

————Time (s)

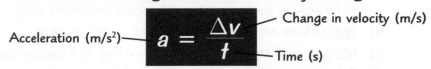

EXAMPLE:
A cat accelerates at 2.5 m/s²
from 2.0 m/s to 6.0 m/s.
Find the time it takes to do this.
$t = \Delta v \div a$
$= (6.0 - 2.0) \div 2.5 = 1.6$ s

4) Deceleration is just negative acceleration (if something slows down, the change in velocity is negative).

You Need to be Able to Estimate Accelerations

You might have to estimate the acceleration (or deceleration) of an object.
To do this, you need the typical speeds from the previous page:

EXAMPLE: A car is travelling along a road, when it collides with a tree and comes to a stop.
Estimate the deceleration of the car.

1) First, give a sensible speed for the car to be travelling at.
2) Next, estimate how long it would take the car to stop.
3) Put these numbers into the acceleration equation.
4) The question asked for the deceleration, so you can lose the minus sign (which shows the car is slowing down):

The typical speed of a car is ~25 m/s.
The car comes to a stop in ~1 s.
$a = \Delta v \div t$
$= (-25) \div 1$
$= -25$ m/s²

The ~ symbol just means it's an approximate value (or answer).

So the deceleration is ~25 m/s²

Uniform Acceleration Means a Constant Acceleration

1) Constant acceleration is sometimes called uniform acceleration.
2) Acceleration due to gravity (g) is uniform for objects in free fall. It's roughly equal to 9.8 m/s² near the Earth's surface and has the same value as gravitational field strength (p.52).
3) You can use this equation for uniform acceleration:

Final velocity (m/s)

$$v^2 - u^2 = 2as$$

Acceleration (m/s²)

Distance (m)

Initial velocity (m/s)

Initial velocity is just the starting velocity of the object.

EXAMPLE: A van travelling at 23 m/s starts decelerating uniformly at 2.0 m/s² as it heads towards
a built-up area 112 m away. What will its speed be when it reaches the built-up area?

1) First, rearrange the equation so v^2 is on one side.
2) Now put the numbers in — remember a is negative because it's a deceleration.
3) Finally, square root the whole thing.

$v^2 = u^2 + 2as$
$v^2 = 23^2 + (2 \times -2.0 \times 112)$
$= 81$
$v = \sqrt{81} = 9$ m/s

Uniform problems — get a clip-on tie or use the equation above...

You might not be told what equation to use in the exam, so make sure you can spot when to use the equation for uniform acceleration. Make a list of the information you're given to help you see what to do.

Q1   A ball is dropped from a height, h, above the ground. The speed of the ball just before it hits the ground is 7 m/s. Calculate the height the ball is dropped from. (acceleration due to gravity ≈ 9.8 m/s²)   [3 marks]

Distance-Time and Velocity-Time Graphs

You need to be able to <u>draw</u> and <u>interpret distance</u> and <u>velocity-time graphs</u>.

You Can Show Journeys on Distance-Time Graphs

If an object moves in a <u>straight line</u>, its <u>distance</u> travelled can be plotted on a <u>distance-time</u> graph.

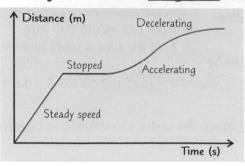

1) <u>Gradient = speed</u>. (The <u>steeper</u> the graph, the <u>faster</u> it's going.)
   This is because: speed = distance ÷ time
   = (change in vertical axis) ÷ (change in horizontal axis).
2) <u>Flat</u> sections are where it's <u>stationary</u> — it's <u>stopped</u>.
3) <u>Straight</u> uphill sections mean it is travelling at a <u>steady speed</u>.
4) <u>Curves</u> represent <u>acceleration</u> or <u>deceleration</u> (p.61).
5) A <u>steepening</u> curve means it's <u>speeding up</u> (increasing gradient).
6) A <u>levelling off</u> curve means it's <u>slowing down</u>.

7) If the object is <u>changing speed</u> (accelerating) you can find its <u>speed at a point</u> by finding the <u>gradient</u> of the <u>tangent</u> to the curve <u>at that point</u>, p.7.

You Can Also Show them on a Velocity-Time Graph

How an object's <u>velocity</u> changes as it travels can be plotted on a <u>velocity-time</u> graph.

1) <u>Gradient = acceleration</u>, since acceleration is change in velocity ÷ time.
2) <u>Flat sections</u> represent travelling at a <u>steady speed</u>.
3) The <u>steeper</u> the graph, the <u>greater</u> the <u>acceleration</u> or <u>deceleration</u>.
4) <u>Uphill</u> sections (/) are <u>acceleration</u>.
5) <u>Downhill</u> sections (\) are <u>deceleration</u>.
6) A <u>curve</u> means <u>changing acceleration</u>.
   If the graph is curved, you can use a tangent to the curve at a point to find the acceleration at that point.

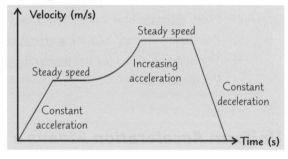

7) The <u>area</u> under any section of the graph (or all of it) is equal to the <u>distance travelled</u> in that <u>time interval</u>.
8) If the section under the graph is <u>irregular</u>, it's easier to find the <u>area</u> by <u>counting the squares</u> under the line and <u>multiplying</u> the number by the value of <u>one square</u>.

EXAMPLE: The velocity-time graph of a car's journey is plotted.
   a) Calculate the acceleration of the car over the first 10 s.
   b) How far does the car travel in the first 15 s of the journey?

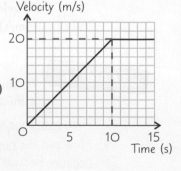

a) This is just the <u>gradient</u> of the line: $a = \Delta v \div t = 20 \div 10 = 2 \text{ m/s}^2$

b) <u>Split</u> the area into a <u>triangle</u> and a <u>rectangle</u>, then <u>add</u> together their areas.
   Or find the <u>value</u> of <u>one square</u>, <u>count</u> the <u>total</u> number of squares under the line, and then <u>multiply</u> these two values together.

   Area = (½ × 10 × 20) + (5 × 20)
   = 200 m

   1 square = 2 m/s × 1 s = 2 m
   Area = 100 squares
   = 100 × 2 = 200 m

Understanding motion graphs — it can be a real uphill struggle...

Make sure you know the difference between distance-time and velocity-time graphs, and how to interpret them.

Q1   Sketch the distance-time graph for an object that accelerates before travelling at a steady speed.   [2 marks]

Q2   A stationary car starts accelerating increasingly for 10 s until it reaches a speed of 20 m/s. It travels at this speed for 20 s until the driver sees a hazard and brakes. He decelerates uniformly, coming to a stop 4 s after braking. Draw the velocity-time graph for this journey.   [3 marks]

Terminal Velocity

Ever wondered why it's so hard to run into a <u>hurricane</u> whilst wearing a <u>sandwich board</u>? Read on to find out...

Friction is Always There to Slow Things Down

1) If an object has <u>no force</u> propelling it along it will always <u>slow down and stop</u> because of <u>friction</u> (unless you're in space where there's nothing to rub against).

2) Friction always acts in the <u>opposite</u> direction to movement.

3) To travel at a <u>steady</u> speed, the driving force needs to <u>balance</u> the frictional forces (see next page).

4) You get friction between <u>two surfaces</u> in contact, or when an object passes <u>through a fluid</u> (drag).

Drag Increases as Speed Increases

1) <u>Drag</u> is the <u>resistance</u> you get in a <u>fluid</u> (a gas or a liquid). <u>Air resistance</u> is a type of <u>drag</u>.

2) The most <u>important factor</u> by far in reducing drag is keeping the shape of the object <u>streamlined</u>. This is where the object is designed to allow fluid to <u>flow easily</u> across it, reducing drag. Parachutes work in the <u>opposite</u> way — they want as much drag as they can get.

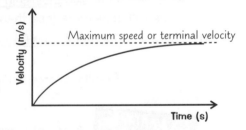
Air flows easily over a streamlined car.

3) <u>Frictional forces</u> from fluids always increase with speed. A car has <u>much more</u> friction to <u>work against</u> when travelling at <u>70 mph</u> compared to <u>30 mph</u>. So at 70 mph the engine has to work <u>much harder</u> just to maintain a <u>steady speed</u>.

Objects Falling Through Fluids Reach a Terminal Velocity

When a falling object first <u>sets off</u>, the force of gravity is <u>much more</u> than the <u>frictional force</u> slowing it down, so it accelerates. As the <u>speed increases</u> the friction <u>builds up</u>. This gradually <u>reduces</u> the <u>acceleration</u> until eventually the <u>frictional force</u> is <u>equal</u> to the <u>accelerating force</u> (so the <u>resultant force is zero</u>). It will have reached its maximum speed or <u>terminal velocity</u> and will fall at a steady speed.

Graph: Velocity (m/s) vs Time (s), showing a curve rising to a dashed horizontal line labelled "Maximum speed or terminal velocity".

Terminal Velocity Depends on Shape and Area

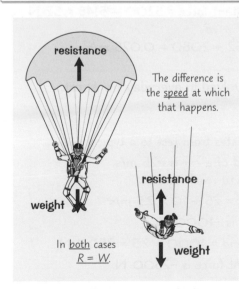

resistance

The difference is the <u>speed</u> at which that happens.

weight

resistance

In <u>both</u> cases <u>R = W</u>.

weight

The <u>accelerating force</u> acting on <u>all</u> falling objects is <u>gravity</u> and it would make them all fall at the <u>same</u> rate if it wasn't for <u>air resistance</u>. This means that on the Moon, where there's <u>no air</u>, hamsters and feathers dropped simultaneously will hit the ground <u>together</u>. However, on Earth, <u>air resistance</u> causes things to fall at <u>different</u> speeds, and the <u>terminal velocity</u> of any object is determined by its <u>drag</u> in <u>comparison</u> to its <u>weight</u>. The frictional force depends on its <u>shape and area</u>.

The most important example is the human <u>skydiver</u>. Without his parachute open he has quite a <u>small</u> area and a force of "<u>W = mg</u>" pulling him down. He reaches a <u>terminal velocity</u> of about <u>120 mph</u>. But with the parachute <u>open</u>, there's much more <u>air resistance</u> (at any given speed) and still only the same force "<u>W = mg</u>" pulling him down. This means his <u>terminal velocity</u> comes down to about <u>15 mph</u>, which is a <u>safe speed</u> to hit the ground at.

Learning about air resistance — it can be a real drag...

Learn what terminal velocity is and why it happens, it's a term that crops up a fair bit in physics.

Q1   Explain why a ball falling from the top of a tall building reaches terminal velocity.   [4 marks]

Newton's First and Second Laws

In the 1660s, a chap called <u>Isaac Newton</u> worked out his dead useful <u>Laws of Motion</u>. Here are the first <u>two</u>.

A Force is Needed to Change Motion

This may seem simple, but it's important. <u>Newton's First Law</u> says that a resultant force (p.53) is needed to make something <u>start moving</u>, <u>speed up</u> or <u>slow down</u>:

> If the resultant force on a <u>stationary</u> object is <u>zero</u>, the object will <u>remain stationary</u>. If the <u>resultant force</u> on a <u>moving</u> object is <u>zero</u>, it'll just carry on moving at the <u>same velocity</u> (same speed <u>and</u> direction).

So, when a train or car or bus or anything else is <u>moving</u> at a <u>constant velocity</u>, the resistive and driving <u>forces</u> on it must all be <u>balanced</u>. The velocity will only change if there's a <u>non-zero</u> resultant force acting on the object.

1) A non-zero <u>resultant</u> force will always produce <u>acceleration</u> (or deceleration) in the <u>direction of the force</u>.

2) This "<u>acceleration</u>" can take <u>five</u> different forms: <u>starting</u>, <u>stopping</u>, <u>speeding up</u>, <u>slowing down</u> and <u>changing direction</u>.

3) On a free body diagram, the <u>arrows</u> will be <u>unequal</u>.

Acceleration is Proportional to the Resultant Force

1) The <u>larger</u> the <u>resultant force</u> acting on an object, the <u>more</u> the object accelerates — the force and the acceleration are <u>directly proportional</u>. You can write this as $F \propto a$.

2) Acceleration is also <u>inversely proportional</u> to the <u>mass</u> of the object — so an object with a <u>larger</u> mass will accelerate <u>less</u> than one with a smaller mass (for a <u>fixed resultant force</u>).

3) There's an incredibly <u>useful formula</u> that describes <u>Newton's Second Law</u>:

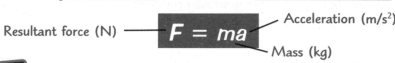

Resultant force (N) ——— $F = ma$ ——— Acceleration (m/s^2)
——— Mass (kg)

EXAMPLE: A van of mass of 2080 kg has an engine that provides a driving force of 5200 N. At 70 mph the drag force acting on the van is 5148 N. Find its acceleration at 70 mph.

1) Work out the <u>resultant force</u> on the van. (Drawing a <u>free body diagram</u> may help.)

    Resultant force = 5200 − 5148 = 52 N

2) <u>Rearrange</u> $F = ma$ and stick in the <u>values</u> you know.

    $a = F \div m$
    = 52 ÷ 2080 = 0.025 m/s^2

You can use <u>Newton's Second Law</u> to get an idea of the forces involved in everyday transport. Large <u>forces</u> are needed to produce large <u>accelerations</u>:

EXAMPLE: Estimate the resultant force on a car as it accelerates from rest to a typical speed.

1) Estimate the <u>acceleration</u> of the car, using <u>typical</u> speeds from page 60. (The ~ means approximately.)

    A typical speed of a car is ~25 m/s.
    It takes ~10 s to reach this.
    So $a = \Delta v \div t = 25 \div 10 = 2.5$ m/s^2

2) <u>Estimate</u> the <u>mass</u> of the car.

    Mass of a car is ~1000 kg.

3) Put these numbers into <u>Newton's 2nd Law</u>.

    So using $F = ma = 1000 \times 2.5 = 2500$ N
    So the resultant force is ~2500 N.

Accelerate your learning — force yourself to revise...

Short and sweet, just how I like my equations. Unfortunately you can't get away with just learning those symbols — make sure you've got your head around both of those laws, before moving on to Newton's third and final law.

Q1   Find the force needed for an 80 kg man on a 10 kg bike to accelerate at 0.25 m/s^2.   [2 marks]

Inertia and Newton's Third Law

Inertia and Newton's Third Law can seem simple on the surface, but they can quickly get confusing. Make sure you really understand what's going on with it — especially if an object is in equilibrium.

Inertia is the Tendency for Motion to Remain Unchanged

1) Until acted upon by a resultant force, objects at rest stay at rest and objects moving at a steady speed will stay moving at that speed (Newton's First Law). This tendency to continue in the same state of motion is called inertia.

2) An object's inertial mass measures how difficult it is to change the velocity of an object.

3) Inertial mass can be found using Newton's Second Law of $F = ma$ (previous page). Rearranging this gives $m = F \div a$, so inertial mass is just the ratio of force over acceleration.

Newton's Third Law: Equal and Opposite Forces Act on Interacting Objects

Newton's Third Law says:

> When two objects interact, the forces they exert on each other are equal and opposite.

1) If you push something, say a shopping trolley, the trolley will push back against you, just as hard.

2) And as soon as you stop pushing, so does the trolley. Kinda clever really.

3) So far so good. The slightly tricky thing to get your head round is this — if the forces are always equal, how does anything ever go anywhere? The important thing to remember is that the two forces are acting on different objects.

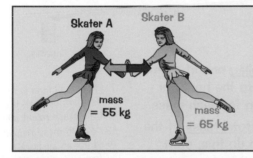

When skater A pushes on skater B, she feels an equal and opposite force from skater B's hand (the 'normal contact' force). Both skaters feel the same sized force, in opposite directions, and so accelerate away from each other.

Skater A will be accelerated more than skater B, though, because she has a smaller mass — remember $a = F \div m$.

An example of Newton's Third Law in an equilibrium situation is a man pushing against a wall. As the man pushes the wall, there is a normal contact force acting back on him. These two forces are the same size. As the man applies a force and pushes the wall, the wall 'pushes back' on him with an equal force.

It can be easy to get confused with Newton's Third Law when an object is in equilibrium. A book resting on the ground is in equilibrium. The weight of the book is equal to the normal contact force.

But this is **NOT** Newton's Third Law because the two forces are different types, and both acting on the book.

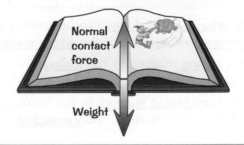

Newton's fourth law — revision must be done with tea...

Newton's 3rd law really trips people up, so make sure you understand exactly what the forces are acting on and how that results in movement (or lack of it). Then have a crack at this question to practise what you know.

Q1   Explain why you don't move when you lean on a wall, even though you are exerting a force.   [3 marks]

 **PRACTICAL**

Investigating Motion

Sure, you can learn the different <u>laws of motion</u>, but doing an experiment for yourself can really help you to understand what's going on. Read on for some snazzy ways to test how <u>mass</u> and <u>force affect motion</u>.

You can Investigate how Mass and Force Affect Acceleration

It's time for an experiment that tests <u>Newton's 2nd law</u>, $F = ma$ (p.64).

1) Set up the apparatus shown below. Set up the <u>trolley</u> so it holds a <u>piece of card</u> with a <u>gap</u> in the middle that will <u>interrupt</u> the signal on the light gate <u>twice</u>. If you measure the <u>length</u> of each bit of card that will pass through the light gate and input this into the <u>software</u>, the light gate can <u>measure</u> the <u>velocity</u> for each bit of card. It can use this to work out the <u>acceleration</u> of the trolley.

2) Connect the trolley to a piece of string that goes over a pulley and is connected on the other side to a hook (that you <u>know</u> the <u>mass</u> of and can <u>add more masses</u> to).

3) The weight of the <u>hook</u> and any <u>masses</u> attached to it will provide the <u>accelerating force</u>, equal to the <u>mass of the hook</u> (m) × <u>acceleration due to gravity</u> (g).

4) The <u>weight</u> of the hook and masses accelerates <u>both</u> the trolley and the masses, so you are investigating the acceleration of the <u>system</u> (the trolley and the masses together).

5) Mark a <u>starting line</u> on the table the trolley is on, so that the trolley always travels the <u>same distance</u> to the light gate.

6) Place the trolley on the <u>starting line</u>, holding the hook so the string is <u>taut</u> (not loose and touching the table), and <u>release</u> it.

7) Record the acceleration measured by the <u>light gate</u> as the trolley passes through it. This is the acceleration of the <u>whole system</u>.

8) Repeat this twice more to get an <u>average acceleration</u>.

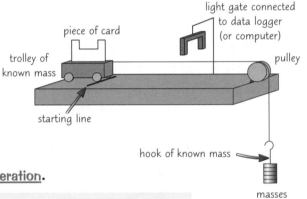

piece of card

light gate connected to data logger (or computer)

trolley of known mass

pulley

starting line

hook of known mass

masses

1) To investigate the <u>effect of mass</u>, <u>add masses</u> to the <u>trolley</u> one at a time to increase the mass of the system. Don't add masses to the hook, or you'll change the force. Record the average <u>acceleration</u> for each mass.

2) To investigate the <u>effect of force</u>, you need to keep the <u>total mass</u> of the system the <u>same</u>, but <u>change</u> the mass on the hook. To do this, start with <u>all</u> the masses loaded onto the <u>trolley</u>, and <u>transfer</u> the masses to the hook one at a time, to increase the <u>accelerating force</u> (the weight of the hanging masses). The mass of the system stays the same as you're only <u>transferring</u> the masses from <u>one part</u> of the system (the trolley) to another (the hook). Record the <u>average acceleration</u> for each <u>force</u>.

The friction between the trolley and the bench might affect your acceleration measurements. You could use an air track to reduce this friction (a track which hovers a trolley on jets of air).

Newton's Second Law Can Explain the Results

1) <u>Newton's Second Law</u> can be written as $F = ma$. Here, F = <u>weight</u> of the <u>hanging masses</u>, m = mass of the <u>whole system</u> and a = <u>acceleration</u> of the <u>system</u>.

2) By <u>adding</u> masses to the <u>trolley</u>, the mass of the <u>whole system</u> increases, but the <u>force</u> applied to the system stays the <u>same</u>. This should lead to a <u>decrease</u> in the <u>acceleration of the trolley</u>, as $a = F \div m$.

3) By <u>transferring masses</u> to the hook, you are <u>increasing the accelerating force</u> without changing the <u>mass</u> of the whole system. So <u>increasing</u> the force should lead to an <u>increase</u> in the acceleration of the trolley.

My acceleration increases with nearby cake...

Know the ins and outs of that experiment — you could be asked about any part of it or to describe the whole thing.

Q1 Explain how a light gate can be used to measure the acceleration of a trolley. [3 marks]

Stopping Distances

Knowing what affects <u>stopping distances</u> is especially useful for everyday life, as well as the exam.

Many Factors Affect Your Total Stopping Distance

1) In an <u>emergency</u> (e.g. a <u>hazard</u> ahead in the road), a driver may perform an <u>emergency stop</u>. This is where <u>maximum force</u> is applied by the <u>brakes</u> in order to stop the car in the <u>shortest possible distance</u>. The <u>longer</u> it takes to perform an <u>emergency stop</u>, the <u>higher the risk</u> of crashing into whatever's in front.

2) The distance it takes to stop a car in an emergency (its <u>stopping distance</u>) is found by:

> **Stopping Distance = Thinking Distance + Braking Distance**

Where the <u>**THINKING DISTANCE**</u> is how far the car travels during the driver's <u>reaction time</u> (the time <u>between</u> the driver <u>seeing</u> a hazard and <u>applying the brakes</u>). And the <u>**BRAKING DISTANCE**</u> is the distance taken to stop under the <u>braking force</u> (once the brakes are applied). Typical <u>car</u> braking distances are: <u>14 m</u> at 30 mph, <u>55 m</u> at 60 mph and <u>75 m</u> at 70 mph.

<u>Thinking distance</u> is affected by:

- Your <u>SPEED</u> — the <u>faster</u> you're going the <u>further</u> you'll travel during the <u>time</u> you take to <u>react</u>.

- Your <u>REACTION TIME</u> — the <u>longer</u> your <u>reaction time</u> (see p.68), the <u>longer</u> your <u>thinking distance</u>.

<u>Braking distance</u> is affected by:

- Your <u>SPEED</u> — for a <u>given</u> braking force, the <u>faster</u> a vehicle travels, the <u>longer</u> it takes to stop.

- The <u>WEATHER</u> or <u>ROAD SURFACE</u> — if it is <u>wet</u> or <u>icy</u>, or there are <u>leaves</u> or <u>oil</u> on the road, there is <u>less grip</u> (and so less <u>friction</u>) between a vehicle's tyres and the road, which can cause tyres to <u>skid</u>.

- The <u>CONDITION</u> of your <u>TYRES</u> — if the tyres of a vehicle are <u>bald</u> (they don't have <u>any tread left</u>) then they cannot <u>get rid of water</u> in wet conditions. This leads to them <u>skidding</u> on top of the water.

- How good your <u>BRAKES</u> are — if brakes are <u>worn</u> or <u>faulty</u>, they won't be able to apply as much <u>force</u> as well-maintained brakes, which could be dangerous when you need to brake hard.

3) You need to be able to <u>describe</u> the <u>factors</u> affecting stopping distance and how this affects <u>safety</u> — especially in an <u>emergency</u>. E.g. <u>icy</u> conditions increase the chance of <u>skidding</u> (and so increase the stopping distance) so driving <u>too close</u> to other cars in icy conditions is <u>unsafe</u>. The <u>longer</u> your stopping distance, the <u>more space</u> you need to leave <u>in front</u> in order to stop <u>safely</u>.

4) <u>Speed limits</u> are really important because <u>speed</u> affects the stopping distance so much.

Braking Relies on Friction Between the Brakes and Wheels

1) When the brake pedal is pushed, this causes brake pads to be <u>pressed</u> onto the wheels. This contact causes <u>friction</u>, which <u>causes work to be done</u>. The work done between the brakes and the wheels transfers <u>energy</u> from the <u>kinetic energy stores</u> of the <u>wheels</u> to the <u>thermal energy stores</u> of the <u>brakes</u>. The brakes <u>increase</u> in <u>temperature</u>.

2) The <u>faster</u> a vehicle is going, the more energy it has in its <u>kinetic</u> stores, so the <u>more work</u> needs to be done to stop it. This means that a <u>greater braking force</u> is needed to make it stop within a <u>certain distance</u>.

3) A larger <u>braking force</u> means a <u>larger deceleration</u>. Very large decelerations can be <u>dangerous</u> because they may cause brakes to <u>overheat</u> (so they don't work as well) or could cause the vehicle to <u>skid</u>.

4) You can <u>estimate</u> the forces involved in <u>accelerations</u> of vehicles using <u>typical values</u>:

EXAMPLE: A car travelling at a typical speed makes an emergency stop to avoid hitting a hazard 25 m ahead. Estimate the braking force needed to produce this deceleration.

1) Assume the deceleration is <u>uniform</u>, and <u>rearrange</u> $v^2 - u^2 = 2as$ to find the deceleration.

2) Then use $F = ma$, with $m = {\sim}1000$ kg.

$v = {\sim}25$ m/s $\quad m = {\sim}1000$ kg.

$a = (v^2 - u^2) \div 2s = (0^2 - 25^2) \div (2 \times 25) = -12.5$

$F = 1000 \times 12.5 = 12\ 500$ N, so F is **~12 500 N**

Stop right there — and learn this page...

Make sure you understand the difference between thinking and braking distance, and the factors affecting them.

Q1 Give one factor that affects braking distance. [1 mark]

Reaction Times

Go long! You need fast <u>reaction times</u> to avoid getting hit in the face when playing catch.

Reaction Times Vary From Person to Person

<u>Everyone's</u> reaction time is different, but a typical reaction time is between <u>0.2</u> and <u>0.9 s</u>.
This can be affected by <u>tiredness</u>, <u>drugs</u> or <u>alcohol</u>. <u>Distractions</u> can also affect your <u>ability</u> to <u>react</u>.

You can Measure Reaction Times with the Ruler Drop Test

You can do <u>simple experiments</u> to investigate your reaction time, but as reaction times
are <u>so short</u>, you haven't got a chance of measuring one with a <u>stopwatch</u>.

One way of measuring reaction times is to use a <u>computer-based test</u>
(e.g. <u>clicking a mouse</u> when the screen changes colour).

Another is the <u>ruler drop test</u>:

1) Sit with your arm resting on the edge of a table
(this should stop you moving your arm up or down during the
test). Get someone else to hold a ruler so it <u>hangs between</u> your
thumb and forefinger, lined up with <u>zero</u>. You may need a <u>third
person</u> to be at <u>eye level with the ruler</u> to check it's lined up.

*ruler hanging between
thumb and forefinger*

*finger in line
with zero*

2) Without giving any warning, the person holding the
ruler should <u>drop it</u>. Close your thumb and finger to
try to <u>catch the ruler as quickly as possible</u>.

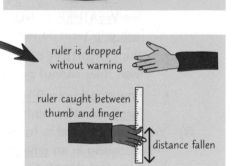

*ruler is dropped
without warning*

*ruler caught between
thumb and finger*

distance fallen

3) The measurement on the ruler at the point where it is caught is
<u>how far</u> the ruler dropped in the time it takes you to react.

4) The <u>longer</u> the <u>distance</u>, the <u>longer</u> the <u>reaction time</u>.

5) You can calculate <u>how long</u> the ruler falls for
(the <u>reaction</u> time) because <u>acceleration due to gravity
is constant</u> (roughly 9.8 m/s²).

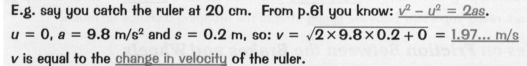

E.g. say you catch the ruler at 20 cm. From p.61 you know: $v^2 - u^2 = 2as$.
$u = 0$, $a = 9.8$ m/s² and $s = 0.2$ m, so: $v = \sqrt{2 \times 9.8 \times 0.2 + 0} = \underline{1.97...}$ m/s
v is equal to the <u>change in velocity</u> of the ruler.
You also know: $\underline{a = \Delta v \div t}$ so $\underline{t = \Delta v \div a = 1.97... \div 9.8 = 0.202... s = 0.2}$ s (to 1 s.f.).
This gives your <u>reaction time</u>.

6) It's <u>pretty hard</u> to do this experiment <u>accurately</u>, so you should do a lot of <u>repeats</u> and calculate
an <u>average</u> reaction time. The results will be better if the ruler falls <u>straight down</u> — you
might want to add a <u>blob of modelling clay</u> to the bottom to stop it from waving about.

7) Make sure it's a <u>fair test</u> — use the <u>same ruler</u> for each repeat, and have the <u>same person</u> dropping it.

8) You could try to investigate some factors affecting reaction time, e.g. you could introduce <u>distractions</u>
by having some <u>music</u> playing or by having someone <u>talk to you</u> while the test takes place.

9) Remember to still do lots of <u>repeats</u> and calculate the <u>mean</u> reaction time with distractions,
which you can <u>compare</u> to the mean reaction time <u>without</u> distractions.

Test a friend's reaction time by throwing this book at them...

Not really. Instead re-read this page and make sure you can describe the experiment. Much more fun.

Q1 Mark's reaction time is tested using the ruler drop test. He is tested in the early afternoon and at night.
In the afternoon, he catches the ruler after it has fallen a distance of 16.2 cm. At night, he catches the ruler
after it has fallen 18.5 cm.
   a) Calculate Mark's reaction time in the afternoon. Give your answer to 2 significant figures. [5 marks]
   b) Explain why Mark's thinking distance might be longer when driving in the evening. [2 marks]

More on Stopping Distances

So now you know what affects <u>stopping distances</u>, let's have a look at the <u>facts</u> and <u>figures</u>.

Leave Enough Space to Stop

1) The figures below for <u>typical stopping distances</u> are from the <u>Highway Code</u>.

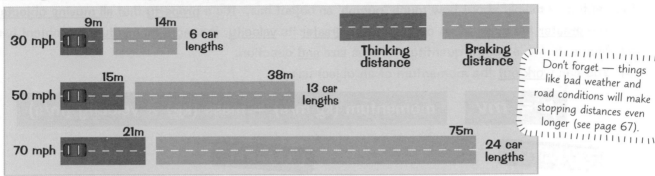

2) To <u>avoid an accident</u>, drivers need to leave <u>enough space</u> between their car and the one in front so that if they had to <u>stop suddenly</u> they would have time to do so <u>safely</u>. 'Enough space' means the <u>stopping distance</u> for whatever speed they're going at.

3) <u>Speed limits</u> are really important because <u>speed</u> affects the stopping distance so much.

Speed Affects Braking Distance More Than Thinking Distance

1) As a car <u>speeds up</u>, the <u>thinking distance increases</u> at the <u>same rate</u> as speed. The graph is <u>linear</u> (a straight line).

2) This is because the thinking time stays pretty <u>constant</u> — but the higher the speed, the more distance you cover in that same time.

3) <u>Braking distance</u>, however, increases <u>faster</u> the more you speed up. The <u>work done</u> to stop the car is <u>equal</u> to the energy in the car's <u>kinetic energy store</u> ($\frac{1}{2}mv^2$). So as speed doubles, the kinetic energy increases <u>4-fold</u> (2^2), and so the <u>work done</u> to stop the car increases 4-fold. Since <u>$W = Fs$</u> (p.53) and the <u>braking force</u> is <u>constant</u>, the <u>braking distance increases 4-fold</u>.

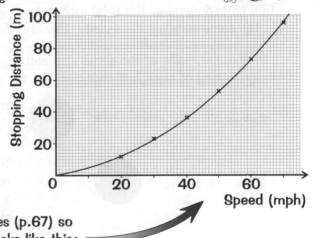

4) <u>Stopping distance</u> is a <u>combination</u> of these two distances (p.67) so the graph of <u>speed</u> against <u>stopping distance</u> for a car looks like this:

5) You need to be able to <u>interpret</u> graphs like this for a <u>range</u> of vehicles — they're all a similar shape.

> **EXAMPLE:** Below is a graph of stopping distance against speed for two vehicles, A and B. Compare the stopping distance for both vehicles at a speed of 40 mph.
>
> 1) Read off the graph to find the <u>stopping distance</u> for each vehicle at <u>40 mph</u>.
>
> Vehicle A stopping distance = 34 m
> Vehicle B stopping distance = 41 m
>
> 2) Find the <u>difference</u> between these two values.
>
> 41 − 34 = 7 m
>
> So the stopping distance for vehicle B is 7 m longer than for vehicle A.
>
>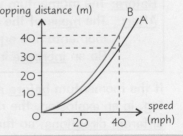

If you live life in the fast lane — leave plenty of space in front...

You have to be comfortable finding information from graphs of stopping distance against speed, so practise it.

Q1 A driver performs an emergency stop. His thinking distance and braking distance are both 6 m. Estimate his total stopping distance if he had been travelling three times as quickly. [4 marks]

Momentum

A large rugby player running very fast has much more momentum than a skinny one out for a Sunday afternoon stroll. It's something that all moving objects have, so you better get your head around it.

Momentum = Mass × Velocity

Momentum is mainly about how much 'oomph' an object has. It's a property that all moving objects have.

1) The greater the mass of an object, or the greater its velocity, the more momentum the object has.

2) Momentum is a vector quantity — it has size and direction.

3) You can work out the momentum of an object using:

$$p = mv$$ momentum (kg m/s) = mass (kg) × velocity (m/s)

EXAMPLE:
A 50 kg cheetah is running at 60 m/s. Calculate its momentum.
$p = mv = 50 \times 60$
$= 3000$ kg m/s

EXAMPLE:
A boy has a mass of 30 kg and a momentum of 75 kg m/s. Calculate his velocity.
$v = p \div m = 75 \div 30 = 2.5$ m/s

Momentum Before = Momentum After

In a closed system, the total momentum before an event (e.g. a collision) is the same as after the event. This is called conservation of momentum.

A closed system is just a fancy way of saying that no external forces act.

In snooker, balls of the same size and mass collide with each other. Each collision is an event where the momentum of each ball changes, but the overall momentum stays the same (momentum is conserved).

Before: m —v→ m

The red ball is stationary, so it has zero momentum. The white ball is moving with a velocity v, so has a momentum of $p = mv$.

After: m → m →

The white ball hits the red ball, causing it to move. The red ball now has momentum. The white ball continues moving, but at a much smaller velocity (and so a much smaller momentum).

The combined momentum of the red and white ball is equal to the original momentum of the white ball, mv.

A moving car hits into the back of a parked car. The crash causes the two cars to lock together, and they continue moving in the direction that the original moving car was travelling, but at a lower velocity.

Before: The momentum was equal to mass of moving car × its velocity.
After: The mass of the moving object has increased, but its momentum is equal to the momentum before the collision. So an increase in mass causes a decrease in velocity.

If the momentum before an event is zero, then the momentum after will also be zero. E.g. in an explosion, the momentum before is zero. After the explosion, the pieces fly off in different directions, so that the total momentum cancels out to zero.

Learn this stuff — it'll only take a moment... um...

Conservation of momentum is incredibly handy — there's more on using it over on the next page.

Q1 Calculate the momentum of a 60 kg woman running at 3 m/s. [2 marks]

Q2 Describe how momentum is conserved by a gun recoiling (moving backwards) as it shoots a bullet. [4 marks]

Changes in Momentum

A <u>force</u> causes the <u>momentum</u> of an object to <u>change</u>. A <u>bigger force</u> makes it change <u>faster</u>.

You Can Use Conservation of Momentum to Calculate Velocities or Masses

You've already seen that <u>momentum is conserved</u> in a <u>closed system</u>.
You can use this to help you calculate things like the <u>velocity</u> or <u>mass</u> of objects in an event.

 **EXAMPLE:** Misha fires a paintball gun. A 3.0 g paintball is fired at a velocity of 90 m/s. Calculate the velocity at which the paintball gun recoils if it has a mass of 1.5 kg. Momentum is conserved.

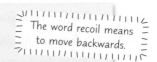
The word recoil means to move backwards.

1) Calculate the <u>momentum</u> of the <u>pellet</u>.

$p = 0.003 \times 90 = 0.27$ kg m/s

2) The momentum before the gun is fired is <u>zero</u>. This is equal to the <u>total</u> momentum after the collision.

Momentum before = momentum after

$0 = 0.27 + (1.5 \times v)$

3) The momentum of the <u>gun</u> is 1.5 × v.

4) <u>Rearrange</u> the equation to find the <u>velocity</u> of the gun. The <u>minus sign</u> shows the gun is travelling in the <u>opposite direction</u> to the bullet.

$v = -(0.27 \div 1.5)$
$= -0.18$ m/s

Forces Cause a Change in Momentum

1) You know that when a non-zero <u>resultant force</u> acts on a moving object (or an object that can move), it causes its <u>velocity</u> to change (p.64). This means that there is a <u>change in momentum</u>.

2) You also know that $F = ma$ and that a = change in velocity ÷ change in time.

Force (N) —— $$F = \frac{m\Delta v}{\Delta t}$$ —— Change in momentum (kg m/s)

—— Change in time (s)

3) So $F = m \times \frac{v - u}{t}$, which can also be written as:

4) The <u>force</u> causing the change is <u>equal</u> to the <u>rate of change of momentum</u>.

5) A <u>larger</u> force means a <u>faster</u> change of momentum.

Equations tell you how variables are related. You should be able to use them to work out how changing one will affect the other.

6) Likewise, if someone's momentum changes <u>very quickly</u> (like in a <u>car crash</u>), the <u>forces</u> on the body will be very <u>large</u>, and more likely to cause <u>injury</u>.

7) This is why cars are designed to slow people down over a <u>longer time</u> when they have a crash — the longer it takes for a change in <u>momentum</u>, the <u>smaller</u> the <u>rate of change of momentum</u>, and so the smaller the <u>force</u>. Smaller forces mean the <u>injuries</u> are likely to be <u>less severe</u>.

<u>Cars</u> have many safety features, such as:
- <u>Crumple zones</u> crumple on impact, increasing the <u>time taken</u> for the <u>car</u> to stop.
- <u>Seat belts stretch</u> slightly, increasing the time taken for the <u>wearer</u> to stop.
- <u>Air bags</u> inflate <u>before</u> you hit the dashboard of a car. The compressing air inside it <u>slows</u> you down more <u>gradually</u> than if you had just hit the <u>hard</u> dashboard.

<u>Bike helmets</u> contain a <u>crushable layer</u> of foam which helps to lengthen the time taken for your <u>head</u> to stop in a crash. This reduces the impact on your <u>brain</u>.

<u>Crash mats</u> and <u>cushioned playground flooring</u> increase the time taken for you to stop if you <u>fall</u> on them. This is because they are made from <u>soft</u>, <u>compressible</u> (squishable) materials.

Don't crumple under the force of revision — take your time...

Make sure you understand how the formula above explains how safety features works.

Q1 A 10 kg object is travelling at 6 m/s. It hits a stationary 20 kg object and the two objects join together and keep moving in the same direction. Calculate the velocity of the combined object, assuming that momentum is conserved.

[3 marks]

Revision Questions for Topic 5

Well, that's <u>Topic 5</u> over and done with — have a quick break then see how you've done with this summary.

- Try these questions and <u>tick off each one</u> when you <u>get it right</u>.
- When you've done <u>all the questions</u> under a heading and are <u>completely happy</u> with it, tick it off.

Forces and Work Done (p.51-54) ☑

1) Explain the difference between scalar and vector quantities, and contact and non-contact forces. ☑
2) What is the formula for calculating the weight of an object? ☑
3) What is a free body diagram? ☑
4) Give the formula for calculating the work done by a force, and explain what each symbol means. ☑
5) How many joules of work does 1 Nm equal? ☑
6) Describe the forces acting on an object in equilibrium. ☑

Stretching and Turning (p.55-57) ☑

7) What is the difference between an elastic and an inelastic deformation? ☑
8) Give the equation that relates force, extension and the spring constant of an object. ☑
9) What is the limit of proportionality? ☑
10) How do you find the following from a linear force-extension graph?   a) spring constant, b) work done ☑
11) Give the equation used to find the energy in an elastic object's elastic potential energy store. ☑
12) Define a moment and state an equation for calculating the size of a moment. ☑
13) If a seesaw is balanced, what can you say about the moments? ☑

Fluid Pressure (p.58-59) ☑

14) State an equation for calculating the pressure at the surface of a fluid. Give the units of pressure. ☑
15) Explain why the pressure increases as you go deeper into a column of a liquid. ☑
16) What causes an object to float? ☑
17) Explain how and why atmospheric pressure varies with height. ☑

Motion (p.60-66) ☑

18) What is the difference between displacement and distance? ☑
19) Define acceleration in terms of velocity and time. ☑
20) What does the term 'uniform acceleration' mean? ☑
21) What does the gradient represent for a) a distance-time graph? b) a velocity-time graph? ☑
22) What is terminal velocity? What causes it? ☑
23) State Newton's three laws of motion. ☑
24) What is inertia? ☑

Car Safety and Momentum (p.67-71) ☑

25) What is the stopping distance of a vehicle? How can it be calculated? ☑
26) State four things that can affect the braking distance of a vehicle. ☑
27) Give two things that affect a person's reaction time. ☑
28) What is an average reaction time? ☑
29) Briefly describe an experiment you could do to compare people's reaction times. ☑
30) State the formula used to calculate an object's momentum. ☑
31) Explain how car safety features use momentum and forces to reduce the risk of injury to passengers. ☑

Transverse and Longitudinal Waves

Waves <u>transfer energy</u> from one place to another <u>without</u> transferring any <u>matter</u> (stuff).

Waves Transfer Energy in the Direction they are Travelling

When waves travel through a medium, the <u>particles</u> of the medium <u>oscillate</u> and <u>transfer energy</u> between each other (see p.11). BUT overall, the particles stay in the <u>same place</u> — <u>only energy</u> is transferred.

For example, if you drop a twig into a calm pool of water, <u>ripples</u> form on the water's surface. The ripples <u>don't</u> carry the <u>water</u> (or the twig) away with them though.
Similarly, if you strum a <u>guitar string</u> and create <u>sound waves</u>, the sound waves don't carry the <u>air</u> away from the guitar and create a <u>vacuum</u>.

1) The <u>amplitude</u> of a wave is the <u>maximum displacement</u> of a point on the wave from its <u>undisturbed position</u>.

2) The <u>wavelength</u> is the distance between the <u>same point</u> on two <u>adjacent</u> waves (e.g. between the <u>trough</u> of one wave and the <u>trough</u> of the wave <u>next to it</u>).

3) <u>Frequency</u> is the <u>number of complete waves</u> passing a certain point <u>per second</u>. Frequency is measured in <u>hertz</u> (Hz). 1 Hz is <u>1 wave per second</u>.

4) From the frequency, you can find the <u>period</u> of a wave using: This is the amount of <u>time</u> it takes for a <u>full cycle</u> of the wave.

5) <u>All waves</u> are either <u>transverse</u> or <u>longitudinal</u> (see below).

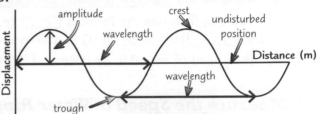

Period (s) — $$T = \frac{1}{f}$$ — Frequency (Hz)

Transverse Waves Have Sideways Vibrations

In <u>transverse waves</u>, the oscillations (vibrations) are <u>perpendicular</u> (at 90°) to the <u>direction</u> of energy transfer. <u>Most waves</u> are transverse, including:

1) <u>All electromagnetic waves</u>, e.g. light (p.76).
2) <u>Ripples</u> and waves in <u>water</u> (see p.74).
3) A wave on a <u>string</u>.

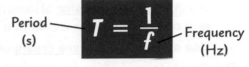

A spring wiggled <u>up and down</u> gives a <u>transverse</u> wave.

vibrations go up and down

wave travels this way

Water waves, shock waves and waves in springs and ropes are all examples of mechanical waves.

Longitudinal Waves Have Parallel Vibrations

In <u>longitudinal waves</u>, the oscillations are <u>parallel</u> to the <u>direction</u> of energy transfer. Examples are:

1) <u>Sound waves</u> in air, <u>ultrasound</u>.
2) <u>Shock waves</u>, e.g. some seismic waves.

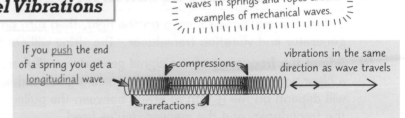

If you <u>push</u> the end of a spring you get a <u>longitudinal</u> wave.

compressions

rarefactions

vibrations in the same direction as wave travels

Wave Speed = Frequency × Wavelength

The <u>wave speed</u> is the speed at which <u>energy is being transferred</u> (or the speed the <u>wave</u> is moving at).
The <u>wave equation</u> applies to <u>all waves</u>:

Wave speed (m/s) — $$v = f\lambda$$ — Wavelength (m)

Frequency (Hz)

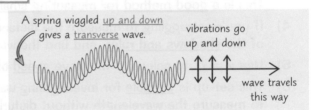

EXAMPLE:

A radio wave has a frequency of 12.0×10^6 Hz. Find its wavelength. (The speed of radio waves in air is 3.0×10^8 m/s.)

$\lambda = v \div f$
$= (3.0 \times 10^8) \div (12.0 \times 10^6) = 25$ m

So, that's the wave basics...

Make sure you've got all this clear in your head, otherwise the rest of the topic will just be a wavey blur of nonsense.

Q1   A wave has a speed of 0.15 m/s and a wavelength of 7.5 cm. Calculate its frequency.   [4 marks]

Experiments With Waves

Time to <u>experiment</u>. Make sure you can choose <u>suitable equipment</u> to measure the <u>speed</u> of <u>different waves</u>.

Use an Oscilloscope to Measure the Speed of Sound

By attaching a <u>signal generator</u> to a speaker you can generate sounds with a specific <u>frequency</u>. You can use <u>two microphones</u> and an <u>oscilloscope</u> to find the <u>wavelength</u> of the sound waves generated.

1) Set up the oscilloscope so the <u>detected waves</u> at each microphone are shown as <u>separate waves</u>.

2) Start with <u>both microphones</u> next to the speaker, then slowly <u>move one away</u> until the two waves are <u>aligned</u> on the display, but have moved <u>exactly one wavelength apart</u>.

3) Measure the <u>distance between the microphones</u> to find one <u>wavelength</u> (λ).

4) You can then use the formula <u>$v = f\lambda$</u> (p.73) to find the <u>speed</u> (v) of the <u>sound waves</u> passing through the <u>air</u> — the <u>frequency</u> (f) is whatever you set the <u>signal generator</u> to (around 1 kHz is sensible).

5) The speed of sound in air is around <u>330 m/s</u>, so check your results <u>roughly agree</u> with this.

speaker attached to signal generator

microphones

oscilloscope

wavelength

waves line up

Measure the Speed of Water Ripples Using a Lamp

PRACTICAL

1) Using a <u>signal generator</u> attached to the <u>dipper</u> of a <u>ripple tank</u> you can create water waves at a <u>set frequency</u>.

2) Use a lamp to see <u>wave crests</u> on a screen below the tank.

3) The distance between each shadow line is equal to one wavelength. Measure the <u>distance</u> between shadow lines that are 10 wavelengths apart, then <u>divide</u> this distance by 10 to find the <u>average wavelength</u>. This is a <u>good method</u> for measuring <u>small</u> wavelengths (p.104).

4) If you're struggling to measure the distance, you could take a <u>photo</u> of the <u>shadows and ruler</u>, and find the wavelength from the photo instead.

5) Use $v = f\lambda$ to calculate the wave <u>speed</u> of the waves.

6) This set-up is <u>suitable</u> for investigating waves, because it allows you to <u>measure</u> the wavelength without <u>disturbing</u> the waves.

lamp

dipper dips in and out of the water producing ripples

to signal generator

screen

water

ruler

shadows cast by ripples

Make sure you dim the lights for this experiment.

You can Use the Wave Equation for Waves on Strings

PRACTICAL

1) Set up the equipment shown on the right, then <u>turn on</u> the signal generator and vibration transducer. The string will start to <u>vibrate</u>.

2) Adjust the <u>frequency</u> of the signal generator until there's a <u>clear wave</u> on the string. The frequency you need will depend on the <u>length</u> of string between the <u>pulley</u> and the <u>transducer</u>, and the <u>masses</u> you've used.

3) You need to measure the <u>wavelength</u> of these waves. The best way to do this <u>accurately</u> is to measure the lengths of, say <u>four or five half-wavelengths</u> (as many as you can) <u>in one go</u>, then <u>divide</u> to get the <u>mean half-wavelength</u> (p.6). You can then <u>double</u> this mean to get a <u>full wavelength</u>.

4) The <u>frequency</u> of the wave is whatever the <u>signal generator</u> is set to.

5) You can find the <u>speed</u> of the wave using $v = f\lambda$.

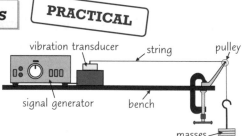

vibration transducer
string
pulley
signal generator
bench
masses

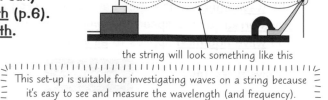

this is the length of 4 half-wavelengths

the string will look something like this

This set-up is suitable for investigating waves on a string because it's easy to see and measure the wavelength (and frequency).

Surf's up, it's time to, like, totally measure some waves...

Sound waves, ripples, and waves on strings are used as model waves because they're easy to work with.

Q1   Describe a suitable experiment to measure the wavelength of a water wave.   [3 marks]

Reflection

If you're anything like me, you'll have spent hours gazing into a <u>mirror</u> in wonder. Here's why...

All Waves Can be Absorbed, Transmitted or Reflected

When waves arrive at a <u>boundary</u> between two <u>different materials</u>, <u>three</u> things can happen:

1) The waves are <u>absorbed</u> by the material the wave is trying to cross into — this <u>transfers energy</u> to the <u>material's energy stores</u> (this is how a microwave works, see page 79).

2) The waves are <u>transmitted</u> — the waves <u>carry on travelling</u> through the new material. This often leads to <u>refraction</u> (see p.76).

3) The waves are <u>reflected</u> — more on this below.

What actually happens depends on the <u>wavelength</u> of the wave and the <u>properties</u> of the <u>materials</u> involved.

You Can Draw a Simple Ray Diagram for Reflection

1) There's <u>one simple rule</u> to learn for <u>all</u> reflected waves:

> ### Angle of incidence = Angle of reflection

2) <u>The angle of incidence</u> is the angle between the <u>incoming wave</u> and the <u>normal</u>.

3) <u>The angle of reflection</u> is the angle between the <u>reflected wave</u> and the normal.

4) The <u>normal</u> is an <u>imaginary line</u> that's <u>perpendicular</u> (at right angles) to the <u>surface</u> at the <u>point of incidence</u> (the point where the wave <u>hits</u> the boundary).

5) The normal is usually shown as a <u>dotted line</u>.

A ray is a line showing the path a wave travels in. It's perpendicular to a wave's wave fronts (next page). Rays are always drawn as straight lines.

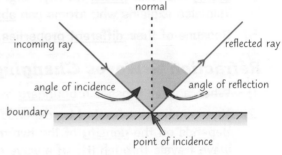

Reflection can be Specular or Diffuse

1) Waves are reflected at <u>different boundaries</u> in <u>different ways</u>. (There's an investigation on this on page 77.)

2) <u>Specular reflection</u> happens when a wave is reflected in a <u>single direction</u> by a <u>smooth surface</u>. E.g. when <u>light</u> is reflected by a <u>mirror</u> you get a nice <u>clear reflection</u>.

3) <u>Diffuse reflection</u> is when a wave is reflected by a <u>rough surface</u> (e.g. a <u>piece of paper</u>) and the reflected rays are <u>scattered</u> in <u>lots of different directions</u>.

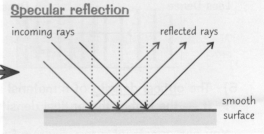

Specular reflection

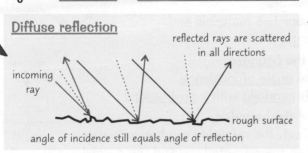

Diffuse reflection

4) This happens because the <u>normal</u> is <u>different</u> for each incoming ray, which means that the <u>angle of incidence is different</u> for each ray. The rule of angle of incidence = angle of reflection <u>still applies</u>.

5) When <u>light</u> is reflected by a rough surface, the surface appears <u>matte</u> (<u>not shiny</u>) and you <u>don't</u> get a <u>clear reflection</u> of objects.

---

*My reflection is absolutely spec*tacular...

Remember, the angle of incidence is always equal to the angle of reflection of a wave.

Q1   Name the type of reflection that occurs when waves are reflected by a smooth mirror.   [1 mark]

Q2   A light ray is incident on a mirror at an angle of 30°. Draw a ray diagram to show its reflection. [3 marks]

Electromagnetic Waves and Refraction

The differences between <u>types</u> of <u>electromagnetic</u> (EM) waves make them useful to us in different ways.

There's a Continuous Spectrum of EM Waves

1) All EM waves are <u>transverse</u> waves (p.73) that transfer energy <u>from a source</u> to an <u>absorber</u>. E.g. a <u>hot object</u> transfers energy by emitting <u>infrared radiation</u>, which is <u>absorbed</u> by the surrounding <u>air</u>.

Electromagnetic waves aren't vibrations of particles, they're vibrations of electric (p.36) and magnetic fields (p.92). This means they can travel through a vacuum.

2) All EM waves travel at the <u>same speed</u> through <u>air</u> or a <u>vacuum</u> (space).

3) Electromagnetic waves form a <u>continuous spectrum</u> over a range of frequencies. They are <u>grouped</u> into <u>seven basic types</u>, based on their <u>wavelength</u> and <u>frequency</u>.

RADIO WAVES	MICRO WAVES	INFRA RED	VISIBLE LIGHT	ULTRA VIOLET	X-RAYS	GAMMA RAYS
$1\,m - 10^4\,m$	$10^{-2}\,m$	$10^{-5}\,m$	$10^{-7}\,m$	$10^{-8}\,m$	$10^{-10}\,m$	$10^{-15}\,m$

Wavelength

INCREASING FREQUENCY AND DECREASING WAVELENGTH

4) There is such a large <u>range of frequencies</u> because EM waves are <u>generated</u> by a <u>variety</u> of changes in <u>atoms</u> and their <u>nuclei</u> (p.43). E.g. changes in the <u>nucleus</u> of an atom creates <u>gamma rays</u> (p.44). This also explains why atoms can <u>absorb</u> a range of frequencies — each one causes a <u>different change</u>.

5) Because of their <u>different properties</u>, different EM waves are used for <u>different purposes</u>.

Refraction — Waves Changing Direction at a Boundary

1) When a wave crosses a <u>boundary</u> between materials at an <u>angle</u> it <u>changes direction</u> — it's <u>refracted</u>.

2) <u>How much</u> it's refracted by depends on how much the wave <u>speeds up</u> or <u>slows down</u>, which usually depends on the <u>density</u> of the two materials (usually the <u>higher</u> the density of a material, the <u>slower</u> a wave travels through it). If a wave crosses a boundary and <u>slows down</u> it will bend <u>towards</u> the <u>normal</u>. If it crosses into a material and <u>speeds up</u> it will bend <u>away</u> from the normal.

3) The <u>wavelength</u> of a wave changes when it is refracted, but the <u>frequency stays the same</u>.

4) If the wave is travelling <u>along the normal</u> it will <u>change speed</u>, but it's <u>NOT refracted</u>.

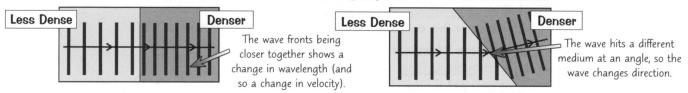

Less Dense   Denser

The wave fronts being closer together shows a change in wavelength (and so a change in velocity).

Less Dense   Denser

The wave hits a different medium at an angle, so the wave changes direction.

5) The <u>optical density</u> of a material is a measure of <u>how quickly light</u> can travel through it — the <u>higher</u> the optical density, the <u>slower</u> light waves travels through it.

You can construct a <u>ray diagram</u> for a <u>refracted light ray</u>.

1) First, start by drawing the <u>boundary</u> between your two materials and the <u>normal</u> (a line that is at 90° to the boundary).

2) Draw an incident <u>ray</u> that <u>meets</u> the <u>normal</u> at the <u>boundary</u>. The angle <u>between</u> the <u>ray</u> and the <u>normal</u> is the <u>angle of incidence</u>. (If you're <u>given</u> this angle, make sure to draw it <u>carefully</u> with a <u>protractor</u>.)

3) Now draw the <u>refracted ray</u> on the other side of the boundary. If the second material is <u>optically denser</u> than first, the refracted ray <u>bends towards</u> the normal (like on the right). The <u>angle</u> between the <u>refracted</u> ray and the <u>normal</u> (the angle of <u>refraction</u>) is <u>smaller</u> than the <u>angle of incidence</u>. If the second material is <u>less optically dense</u>, the angle of refraction is <u>larger</u> than the angle of incidence.

incoming ray
angle of incidence
boundary
normal
angle of refraction
refracted ray

Lights, camera, refraction...

Refraction comes up again and again in GCSE Physics, so make sure you really understand it before moving on.

Q1   Draw a ray diagram for a light ray entering a less optically dense medium at 40° to the normal.   [3 marks]

Investigating Light

Hurrah — it's time to whip out your ray box and get some <u>reflection</u> and <u>refraction</u> going on...

You Need to Do Both of These Experiments in a Dim Room

<u>Both</u> experiments use <u>rays of light</u>, so it's best to do them in a <u>dim room</u> so you can <u>clearly</u> see the light rays. They also both use either a <u>ray box</u> or a <u>laser</u> to produce <u>thin</u> rays of light. This is so you can easily see the <u>middle</u> of the ray when <u>tracing</u> it and <u>measuring angles</u> from it.

You Can Use Transparent Materials to Investigate Refraction

The boundaries between <u>different substances</u> refract light by <u>different amounts</u>. You can investigate this by looking at how much light is <u>refracted</u> when it passes from <u>air</u> into <u>different materials</u>.

1) Place a transparent rectangular block on a piece of <u>paper</u> and <u>trace around it</u>. Use a <u>ray box</u> or a <u>laser</u> to shine a ray of light at the <u>middle</u> of one side of the block.

2) <u>Trace</u> the <u>incident ray</u> and <u>mark</u> where the light ray <u>emerges</u> on the other side of the block. Remove the block and, with a <u>straight line</u>, <u>join up</u> the <u>incident ray</u> and the emerging point to show the path of the <u>refracted ray</u> through the block.

3) Draw the <u>normal</u> at the <u>point</u> where the light ray entered the block. Use a protractor to measure the <u>angle</u> between the <u>incident</u> ray and the <u>normal</u> (the <u>angle of incidence</u>, *I*) and the angle between the <u>refracted</u> ray and the <u>normal</u> (the <u>angle of refraction</u>, *R*).

4) <u>Repeat</u> this experiment using rectangular blocks made from different materials, keeping the <u>incident angle</u> the <u>same</u> throughout.

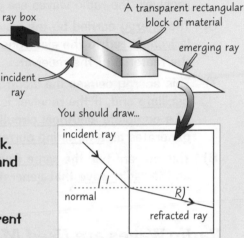

You should find that the angle of refraction <u>changes</u> for different materials — this difference is due to their different <u>optical densities</u> (see page 76).

Different Materials Reflect Light by Different Amounts

1) Take a piece of paper and <u>draw a straight line across it</u>. Place an object so one of its sides <u>lines up</u> with this line.

2) Shine a <u>ray</u> of light at the object's surface and <u>trace</u> the <u>incoming</u> and <u>reflected</u> light beams.

3) Draw the <u>normal</u> at the point where the ray hits the object. Use a protractor to measure the angle of <u>incidence</u> and the <u>angle of reflection</u> and <u>record</u> these values in a table. Also make a note of the <u>width</u> and <u>brightness</u> of the <u>reflected</u> light ray.

4) <u>Repeat</u> this experiment for a range of <u>objects</u>.

For a refresher on reflection, go back to page 75.

You should also see that <u>smooth</u> surfaces like mirrors give <u>clear reflections</u> (the reflected ray is as <u>thin</u> and <u>bright</u> as the <u>incident</u> ray). <u>Rough</u> surfaces like paper cause <u>diffuse</u> reflection (p.75) which causes the reflected beam to be <u>wider and dimmer</u> (or <u>not observable at all</u>).

You should also find that the <u>angle of incidence ALWAYS equals the angle of reflection</u>.

Time to reflect...

These experiments aren't the trickiest, but you still have to be able to describe how to do them and what they show.

Q1   a) Describe an experiment you could do to measure how much light is refracted by different materials.   **[4 marks]**

       b) Explain why a thin beam of light should be used.   **[1 mark]**

Radio Waves

EM waves are used for all sorts of stuff — and radio waves are definitely the most entertaining.
They transfer energy to your car radio and your TV — what would you do without them?

Radio Waves are Made by Oscillating Charges

1) EM waves are made up of oscillating electric and magnetic fields.

2) Alternating currents (ac) (p.31) are made up of oscillating charges. As the charges oscillate, they produce oscillating electric and magnetic fields, i.e. electromagnetic waves.

3) The frequency of the waves produced will be equal to the frequency of the alternating current.

4) You can produce radio waves using an alternating current in an electrical circuit. The object in which charges (electrons) oscillate to create the radio waves is called a transmitter.

5) When transmitted radio waves reach a receiver, the radio waves are absorbed.

6) The energy carried by the waves is transferred to the electrons in the material of the receiver.

7) This energy causes the electrons to oscillate and, if the receiver is part of a complete electrical circuit, it generates an alternating current.

8) This current has the same frequency as the radio wave that generated it.

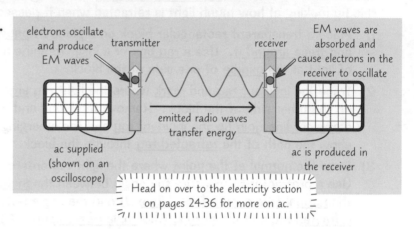

electrons oscillate and produce EM waves — transmitter — receiver — EM waves are absorbed and cause electrons in the receiver to oscillate

ac supplied (shown on an oscilloscope)

emitted radio waves transfer energy

ac is produced in the receiver

Head on over to the electricity section on pages 24-36 for more on ac.

Radio Waves are Used Mainly for Communication

1) Radio waves are EM radiation with wavelengths longer than about 10 cm.

2) Long-wave radio (wavelengths of 1 – 10 km) can be transmitted from London, say, and received halfway round the world. That's because long wavelengths diffract (bend) around the curved surface of the Earth. Long-wave radio wavelengths can also diffract around hills, into tunnels and all sorts.

3) This makes it possible for radio signals to be received even if the receiver isn't in line of the sight of the transmitter.

4) Short-wave radio signals (wavelengths of about 10 m – 100 m) can, like long-wave, be received at long distances from the transmitter. That's because they are reflected (see p.75) from the ionosphere — an electrically charged layer in the Earth's upper atmosphere.

5) Bluetooth® uses short-wave radio waves to send data over short distances between devices without wires (e.g. wireless headsets so you can use your phone while driving a car).

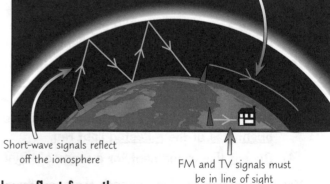

Long-wave signals bend around the Earth

Short-wave signals reflect off the ionosphere

FM and TV signals must be in line of sight

6) Medium-wave signals (well, the shorter ones) can also reflect from the ionosphere, depending on atmospheric conditions and the time of day.

7) The radio waves used for TV and FM radio transmissions have very short wavelengths. To get reception, you must be in direct sight of the transmitter — the signal doesn't bend or travel far through buildings.

Size matters — and my wave's longer than yours...

Producing radio waves — who knew it was so tricky? It's worth it though — they're just so darn useful.

Q1   State one use of radio waves.   [1 mark]

Q2   Describe how radio waves can be produced.   [1 mark]

EM Waves and Their Uses

Radio waves aren't the only waves used for communication — other EM waves come in pretty handy too. The most important thing is to think about how the properties of a wave relate to its uses.

Microwaves are Used by Satellites

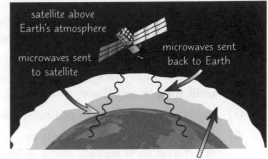

satellite above Earth's atmosphere

microwaves sent to satellite

microwaves sent back to Earth

cloud and water vapour

1) Communication to and from satellites (including satellite TV signals and satellite phones) uses microwaves. But you need to use microwaves which can pass easily through the Earth's watery atmosphere.

2) For satellite TV, the signal from a transmitter is transmitted into space...

3) ... where it's picked up by the satellite receiver dish orbiting thousands of kilometres above the Earth. The satellite transmits the signal back to Earth in a different direction...

4) ... where it's received by a satellite dish on the ground. There is a slight time delay between the signal being sent and received because of the long distance the signal has to travel.

Microwave Ovens Use a Different Wavelength from Satellites

1) In communications, the microwaves used need to pass through the Earth's watery atmosphere.

2) In microwave ovens, the microwaves need to be absorbed by water molecules in food — so they use a different wavelength to those used in satellite communications.

3) The microwaves penetrate up to a few centimetres into the food before being absorbed and transferring the energy they are carrying to the water molecules in the food, causing the water to heat up.

4) The water molecules then transfer this energy to the rest of the molecules in the food by heating — which quickly cooks the food.

Infrared Radiation Can be Used to Increase or Monitor Temperature

1) Infrared (IR) radiation is given out by all hot objects — and the hotter the object, the more IR radiation it gives out.

2) Infrared cameras can be used to detect infrared radiation and monitor temperature. The camera detects the IR radiation and turns it into an electrical signal, which is displayed on a screen as a picture. The hotter an object is, the brighter it appears. E.g. energy transfer from a house's thermal energy store can be detected using infrared cameras.

Different colours represent different amounts of IR radiation being detected. Here, the redder the colour, the more infrared radiation is being detected.

3) Absorbing IR radiation causes objects to get hotter. Food can cooked using IR radiation — the temperature of the food increases when it absorbs IR radiation, e.g. from a toaster's heating element.

4) Electric heaters heat a room in the same way. Electric heaters contain a long piece of wire that heats up when a current flows through it. This wire then emits lots of infrared radiation (and a little visible light — the wire glows). The emitted IR radiation is absorbed by objects and the air in the room — energy is transferred by the IR waves to the thermal energy stores of the objects, causing their temperature to increase.

Revision time — adjust depending on brain wattage...

The next time you're feeling hungry and zap some food in the microwave, think of it as doing revision.

Q1   Explain why signals between satellites are transmitted as microwaves.   [1 mark]

More Uses of EM Waves

Haven't had enough <u>uses of EM waves</u>? Good, because here are just a few more uses of those incredibly handy waves — complete with the all-important <u>reasons</u> for why they have been used. Get learning.

Fibre Optic Cables Use Visible Light to Transmit Data

1) <u>Optical fibres</u> are thin <u>glass or plastic fibres</u> that can <u>carry data</u> (e.g. from telephones or computers) over long distances as pulses of <u>visible light</u>.

2) They work because of <u>reflection</u> (p.75). The light rays are <u>bounced back and forth</u> until they reach the end of the fibre.

3) <u>Visible light</u> is used in optical fibres.

4) Light is not easily <u>absorbed</u> or <u>scattered</u> as it travels along a fibre.

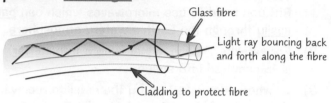

Glass fibre

Light ray bouncing back and forth along the fibre

Cladding to protect fibre

Ultraviolet Radiation Gives You a Suntan

1) <u>Fluorescence</u> is a property of certain chemicals, where <u>ultra-violet</u> (<u>UV</u>) radiation is <u>absorbed</u> and then <u>visible light</u> is <u>emitted</u>. That's why fluorescent colours look so <u>bright</u> — they actually <u>emit light</u>.

2) <u>Fluorescent lights</u> generate <u>UV radiation</u>, which is absorbed and <u>re-emitted as visible light</u> by a layer of <u>phosphorus</u> on the inside of the bulb. They're <u>energy-efficient</u> (p.17) so they're good to use when light is needed for <u>long periods</u> (like in your <u>classroom</u>).

3) <u>Security pens</u> can be used to <u>mark</u> property with your name (e.g. laptops). Under <u>UV light</u> the ink will <u>glow</u> (fluoresce), but it's <u>invisible</u> otherwise. This can help the police <u>identify</u> your property if it's stolen.

4) <u>Ultraviolet radiation (UV)</u> is produced by the Sun, and exposure to it is what gives people a <u>suntan</u>.

5) When it's <u>not sunny</u>, some people go to <u>tanning salons</u> where <u>UV lamps</u> are used to give them an artificial <u>suntan</u>. However, overexposure to UV radiation can be <u>dangerous</u> (fluorescent lights emit very little UV — they're totally safe).

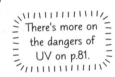

There's more on the dangers of UV on p.81.

X-rays and Gamma Rays are Used in Medicine

1) <u>Radiographers</u> in <u>hospitals</u> take <u>X-ray 'photographs'</u> of people to see if they have any <u>broken bones</u>.

2) X-rays pass <u>easily through flesh</u> but not so easily through <u>denser material</u> like <u>bones</u> or <u>metal</u>. So it's the amount of radiation that's <u>absorbed</u> (or <u>not absorbed</u>) that gives you an X-ray image.

3) <u>Radiographers</u> use <u>X-rays</u> and <u>gamma rays</u> to treat people with <u>cancer</u> (radiotherapy). This is because high doses of these rays <u>kill all living cells</u> — so they are carefully <u>directed</u> towards cancer cells, to avoid killing too many normal, <u>healthy cells</u>.

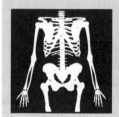

The <u>brighter bits</u> are where <u>fewer X-rays</u> get through. This is a <u>negative image</u>. The plate starts off <u>all white</u>.

There's more on gamma rays on p.44.

4) Gamma radiation can also be used as a <u>medical tracer</u> (p.48) — this is where a <u>gamma-emitting source</u> is injected into the patient, and its <u>progress</u> is followed around the body. Gamma radiation is well <u>suited</u> to this because it can <u>pass out</u> through the body to be <u>detected</u>.

5) <u>Both</u> X-rays and gamma rays can be <u>harmful</u> to people (p.81), so radiographers wear <u>lead aprons</u> and stand behind a <u>lead screen</u> or <u>leave the room</u> to keep their exposure to them to a minimum.

Don't lie to an X-ray — they can see right through you...

I hate to say it, but go back to page 78 and read all of the uses for EM waves again to really learn them.

Q1 State two uses of X-rays. [2 marks]

Q2 Explain why plastic optical fibres use pulses of visible light to transmit data. [1 mark]

Dangers of Electromagnetic Waves

Okay, so you know how <u>useful</u> electromagnetic radiation can be — well, it can also be pretty <u>dangerous</u>.

Some EM Radiation Can be Harmful to People

1) When EM radiation enters <u>living tissue</u> — like <u>you</u> — it's often harmless, but sometimes it creates havoc. The effects of each type of radiation are based on <u>how much energy the wave transfers</u>.

2) <u>Low frequency</u> waves, like <u>radio waves</u>, don't transfer much energy and so mostly <u>pass through soft tissue</u> without being absorbed.

3) <u>High frequency</u> waves like <u>UV</u>, <u>X-rays</u> and <u>gamma rays</u> all transfer <u>lots</u> of energy and so can cause <u>lots of damage</u>.

4) <u>UV radiation</u> damages surface cells, which can lead to <u>sunburn</u> and cause <u>skin</u> to <u>age prematurely</u>. Some more serious effects are <u>blindness</u> and an <u>increased risk of skin cancer</u>.

5) <u>X-rays</u> and <u>gamma rays</u> are types of <u>ionising radiation</u>. (They carry enough energy to <u>knock electrons off of atoms</u>.) This can cause <u>gene mutation or cell destruction</u>, and <u>cancer</u>.

You Can Measure Risk Using the Radiation Dose in Sieverts

1) Whilst UV radiation, X-rays and gamma rays can all be <u>harmful</u>, they are also very <u>useful</u> (see pages 78-80). <u>Before</u> any of these types of EM radiation are used, people look at whether the <u>benefits outweigh the health risks</u>.

2) For example, the <u>risk</u> of a person involved in a car accident developing cancer from having an X-ray photograph taken is <u>much smaller</u> than the potential health risk of not finding and treating their injuries.

3) <u>Radiation dose</u> (measured in <u>sieverts</u>) is a measure of the <u>risk</u> of harm from the body being exposed to radiation.

4) This is <u>not</u> a measure of the <u>total amount</u> of radiation that has been <u>absorbed</u>.

5) The risk depends on the <u>total amount of radiation</u> absorbed <u>and</u> how <u>harmful</u> the <u>type</u> of radiation is.

6) A sievert is pretty big, so you'll often see doses in <u>millisieverts</u> (mSv), where <u>1000 mSv = 1 Sv</u>.

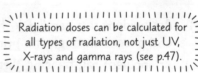
Radiation doses can be calculated for all types of radiation, not just UV, X-rays and gamma rays (see p.47).

Risk can be Different for Different Parts of the Body

A CT scan uses <u>X-rays</u> and a <u>computer</u> to build up a picture of the inside of a patient's body. The table shows the <u>radiation dose</u> received by two <u>different parts</u> of a patient's body when having CT scans.

	Radiation dose (mSv)
Head	2.0
Chest	8.0

If a patient has a CT scan on their <u>chest</u>, they are <u>four times more likely</u> to suffer damage to their genes (and their <u>added risk</u> of harm is <u>four times higher</u>) than if they had a <u>head</u> scan.

This is not an excuse to stay in bed all day...

It's impossible to avoid all forms of harmful radiation, so it's all about balancing risks and reducing your exposure.

Q1 Give two effects of a person being exposed to too much UV radiation. [2 marks]

Q2 A patient's pelvis is being examined. It can either be examined with a single X-ray photograph or with a CT scan. An X-ray of the pelvis has a radiation dose of 0.7 mSv. A CT scan of the pelvis has a radiation dose of 7 mSv. How much larger is the added risk of harm if the patient has a CT scan? [1 mark]

Lenses

These next few pages are about how <u>light</u> acts when it hits a <u>lens</u>. Be ready for lots of <u>diagrams</u>.

Different Lenses Produce Different Kinds of Image

Lenses form images by <u>refracting</u> light (p.76) and changing its direction. There are <u>two main types</u> of lens — <u>convex</u> and <u>concave</u>. They have different shapes and have <u>opposite effects</u> on light rays.

1) A <u>convex</u> lens <u>bulges outwards</u>. It causes rays of <u>light</u> parallel to the axis to be <u>brought together</u> (<u>converge</u>) at the <u>principal focus</u>.

2) A <u>concave</u> lens <u>caves inwards</u>. It causes parallel rays of <u>light</u> to <u>spread out</u> (<u>diverge</u>).

3) The <u>axis</u> of a lens is a line passing through the <u>middle</u> of the lens.

4) The <u>principal focus</u> of a <u>convex lens</u> is where rays hitting the lens parallel to the axis all <u>meet</u>.

5) The <u>principal focus</u> of a <u>concave lens</u> is the point where rays hitting the lens parallel to the axis <u>appear</u> to all <u>come from</u> — you can trace them back until they all appear to <u>meet up</u> at a point behind the lens.

6) There is a principal focus on <u>each side</u> of the lens. The <u>distance</u> from the <u>centre of the lens</u> to the <u>principal focus</u> is called the <u>focal length</u>.

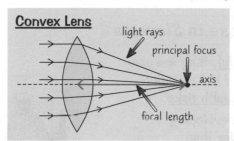

Convex Lens — light rays, principal focus, axis, focal length

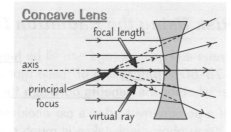

Concave Lens — focal length, axis, principal focus, virtual ray

> Convex lenses are also called converging lenses, and concave lenses are called diverging lenses.

> The difference between real and virtual is explained on the next page.

You need to make sure you can draw proper <u>ray diagrams</u> to show how convex and concave lenses <u>differ</u> — see pages 83-84.

There are Three Rules for Refraction in a Convex Lens...

1) An incident ray <u>parallel to the axis</u> refracts through the lens and passes through the <u>principal focus</u> on the other side.

2) An incident ray passing <u>through the principal focus</u> refracts through the lens and travels <u>parallel to the axis</u>.

3) An incident ray passing through the <u>centre</u> of the lens carries on in the <u>same direction</u>.

> An example ray diagram for a convex lens is on page 83.

...And Three Rules for Refraction in a Concave Lens

1) An incident ray <u>parallel to the axis</u> refracts through the lens, and travels in line with the <u>principal focus</u> (so it appears to have come from the principal focus).

2) An incident ray passing through the lens <u>towards the principal focus</u> refracts through the lens and travels <u>parallel to the axis</u>.

3) An incident ray passing through the <u>centre</u> of the lens carries on in the <u>same direction</u>.

The <u>neat thing</u> about these rules is that they allow you to draw ray diagrams <u>without</u> bending the rays as they go into the lens <u>and</u> as they leave the lens. You can draw the diagrams as if each ray only changes direction <u>once</u>, in the <u>middle of the lens</u> (see next page).

Warning — too much revision can cause a loss of focus...

Those rules are dead important for drawing ray diagrams, which you'll see loads of on the next page.

Q1　What is the principal focus of:　　a) a convex lens　　b) a concave lens?　　　　　[2 marks]

Q2　Sketch parallel rays of light being focused by a convex lens.　　　　　[2 marks]

Topic 6 — Waves

Images and Ray Diagrams

Lenses can create <u>virtual</u> or <u>real images</u> (don't worry, it's not as weird as it sounds). After working through this page, you should be able to draw a <u>ray diagram</u> for a <u>convex</u> lens and know the <u>type of image</u> that's created.

Lenses can Produce Real and Virtual Images

1) A <u>real image</u> is where the <u>light from an object</u> comes together to form an <u>image on a 'screen'</u> — like the image formed on an eye's <u>retina</u> (the 'screen' at the back of an <u>eye</u>).

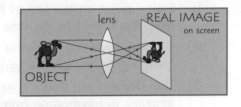

2) A <u>virtual image</u> is when the rays are diverging, so the light from the object <u>appears</u> to be coming from a completely <u>different place</u>.

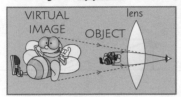

3) When you look in a <u>mirror</u> you see a <u>virtual image</u> of your face — because the <u>object</u> (your face) <u>appears</u> to be <u>behind the mirror</u>.

4) You can get a virtual image when looking at an object through a <u>magnifying lens</u> (see next page) — the virtual image looks <u>bigger</u> than the object <u>actually</u> is.

To describe an image properly, you need to say <u>3 things</u>: 1) <u>How big it is</u> compared to the object; 2) Whether it's <u>upright or inverted</u> (upside down) relative to the object; 3) Whether it's <u>real or virtual</u>.

Draw a Ray Diagram for an Image Through a Convex Lens

1) Pick a point on the <u>top</u> of the object. Draw a ray going from the object to the lens <u>parallel</u> to the axis of the lens.

2) Draw another ray from the <u>top</u> of the object going right through the <u>middle</u> of the lens.

3) The incident ray that's <u>parallel</u> to the axis is <u>refracted</u> through the <u>principal focus</u> (F) on the <u>other side</u> of the lens. Draw a <u>refracted ray</u> passing through the <u>principal focus</u>.

4) The ray passing through the <u>middle</u> of the lens doesn't bend.

5) Mark where the rays <u>meet</u>. That's the <u>top of the image</u>.

6) Repeat the process for a point on the bottom of the object. When the bottom of the object is on the <u>axis</u>, the bottom of the image is <u>also</u> on the axis.

In ray diagrams, this represents a convex lens.

If you <u>really</u> want to draw a <u>third incident ray</u> passing through the <u>principal focus</u> on the way to the lens, you can (refract it so that it goes <u>parallel to the axis</u>). In the <u>exam</u>, you can get away with <u>two rays</u>, so no need to bother with three.

Distance from the Lens Affects the Image

1) An object <u>at 2F</u> will produce a <u>real</u>, <u>inverted</u> image the <u>same size</u> as the object, and <u>at 2F</u>.

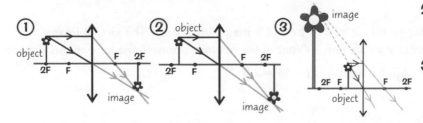

2) <u>Between F and 2F</u> it'll make a <u>real</u>, <u>inverted</u> image <u>bigger</u> than the object, and <u>beyond 2F</u>.

3) An object <u>nearer than F</u> will make a <u>virtual</u> image the <u>right way up</u>, <u>bigger</u> than the object, on the <u>same side</u> of the lens.

Virtual images — they're not just in video games...

Make sure you know the differences between real and virtual images, they can be pretty tough.

Q1 Draw a ray diagram for an object at a distance of 2F in front of a convex lens. [3 marks]

Concave Lenses and Magnification

Now for <u>concave lenses</u> and getting up close and personal with a handy equation — the <u>magnification formula</u>.

Draw a Ray Diagram for an Image Through a Concave Lens

1) Pick a point on the <u>top</u> of the object. Draw a ray going from the object to the lens <u>parallel</u> to the axis of the lens.

2) Draw another ray from the <u>top</u> of the object going right through the <u>middle</u> of the lens.

3) The incident ray that's <u>parallel</u> to the axis is <u>refracted</u> so it appears to have come from the <u>principal focus</u>. Draw a <u>ray</u> from the principal focus. Make it <u>dotted</u> before it reaches the lens.

4) The ray passing through the <u>middle</u> of the lens doesn't bend.

5) Mark where the refracted rays <u>meet</u>. That's the top of the image.

6) Repeat the process for a point on the bottom of the object. When the bottom of the object is on the <u>axis</u>, the bottom of the image is <u>also</u> on the axis.

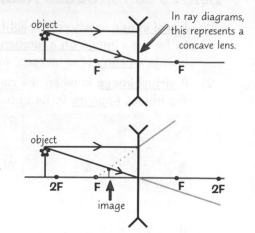

In ray diagrams, this represents a concave lens.

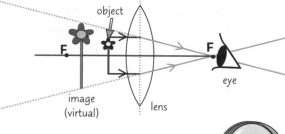

Concave Lenses Always Create Virtual Images

Unlike a <u>convex</u> lens, a <u>concave</u> lens always produces a <u>virtual image</u>. The image is <u>right way up</u>, <u>smaller</u> than the object and on the <u>same side of the lens as the object</u> — <u>no matter where the object is</u>.

Magnifying Glasses Use Convex Lenses

Magnifying glasses work by creating a <u>magnified virtual image</u>.

1) The object being magnified must be closer to the lens than the <u>focal length</u>.

2) Since the image produced is a <u>virtual image</u>, the light rays don't <u>actually</u> come from the place where the image appears to be.

3) Remember "you <u>can't</u> project a virtual image onto a screen" — that's a <u>useful phrase</u> to use in the exam if they ask you about virtual images.

4) You can use the <u>magnification formula</u> to work out the magnification produced by a <u>lens</u> at a given distance:

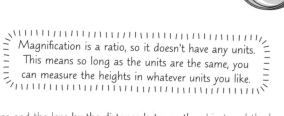

$$\text{magnification} = \frac{\text{image height}}{\text{object height}}$$

Magnification is a ratio, so it doesn't have any units. This means so long as the units are the same, you can measure the heights in whatever units you like.

(You can also find the magnification by dividing the <u>distance</u> between the <u>image and the lens</u> by the distance between the <u>object and the lens</u>.)

EXAMPLE: A coin with diameter 14 mm is placed behind a magnifying lens. The virtual image produced has a diameter of 35 mm. What is the magnification of the lens at this distance?

magnification = image height ÷ object height = 35 ÷ 14 = 2.5

If you ask me, lenses are magnificent...

Congratulations, you've reached the end of lenses. Why not celebrate with some practice questions?

Q1 Find the magnification of a lens if a 12 cm tall object produces a 6 cm high image. [2 marks]

Q2 Calculate the height of an image if the object is 10 cm tall and the magnification is 2.5. [3 marks]

Visible Light

Ah, light. That stuff we see all of the time. But it's a bit more complicated than you might have thought.

Visible Light is Made Up of a Range of Colours

1) As you saw on page 76, EM waves cover a very large spectrum. We can only see a tiny part of this — the visible light spectrum. This is a range of wavelengths that we perceive as different colours.

2) Each colour has its own narrow range of wavelengths (and frequencies) ranging from violets down at 400 nm up to reds at 700 nm.

3) Colours can also mix together to make other colours. The only colours you can't make by mixing are the primary colours: pure red, green and blue.

4) When all of these different colours are put together, it creates white light.

Colour and Transparency Depend on Absorbed Wavelengths

1) Different objects absorb, transmit and reflect different wavelengths of light in different ways (p.75).

2) Opaque objects are objects that do not transmit light. When visible light waves hit them, they absorb some wavelengths of light and reflect others.

3) The colour of an opaque object depends on which wavelengths of light are most strongly reflected. E.g. a red apple appears to be red because the wavelengths corresponding to the red part of the visible spectrum are most strongly reflected. The other wavelengths of light are absorbed.

4) For opaque objects that aren't a primary colour, they may be reflecting either the wavelengths of light corresponding to that colour OR the wavelengths of the primary colours that can mix together to make that colour. So a banana may look yellow because it's reflecting yellow light OR because it's reflecting both red and green light.

5) White objects reflect all of the wavelengths of visible light equally.

6) Black objects absorb all wavelengths of visible light. Your eyes see black as the lack of any visible light (i.e. the lack of any colour).

7) Transparent (see-through) and translucent (partially see-through) objects transmit light, i.e. not all light that hits the surface of the object is absorbed or reflected — some can pass through.

8) Some wavelengths of light may be absorbed or reflected by transparent and translucent objects. A transparent or translucent object's colour is related to the wavelengths of light transmitted and reflected by it.

Colour Filters Only Let Through Particular Wavelengths

1) Colour filters are used to filter out different wavelengths of light, so that only certain colours (wavelengths) are transmitted — the rest are absorbed.

2) A primary colour filter only transmits that colour, e.g. if white light is shone at a blue colour filter, only blue light will be let through. The rest of the light will be absorbed.

3) If you look at a blue object through a blue colour filter, it would still look blue. Blue light is reflected from the object's surface and is transmitted by the filter.

4) However, if the object was e.g. red (or any colour not made from blue light), the object would appear black when viewed through a blue filter. All of the light reflected by the object will be absorbed by the filter.

5) Filters that aren't for primary colours let through both the wavelengths of light for that colour AND the wavelengths of the primary colours that can be added together to make that colour.

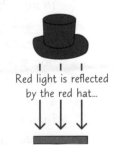

Red light is reflected by the red hat...

...but it's not transmitted by the blue colour filter...

...so the hat appears black.

Have you seen my white shirt? It's red and green and blue...

Remember that the colour of an opaque object depends on the wavelengths of visible light it most strongly reflect.

Q1 A student looks at a red bag with a green buckle through a green colour filter. Describe and explain the appearance of the bag and the buckle when the student looks through the filter. [4 marks]

Infrared Radiation and Temperature

Fun Fact — although the radiators in most houses are painted <u>white</u>, they'd actually do their job better if you painted them <u>black</u>. It'd ruin with the colour scheme in my sitting room though...

Every Object Absorbs and Emits Infrared Radiation

1) <u>All objects</u> are <u>continually emitting</u> and <u>absorbing infrared</u> (IR) radiation. Infrared radiation is emitted from the <u>surface</u> of an object.

2) The <u>hotter</u> an object is, the <u>more</u> infrared radiation it radiates in a given time.

3) An object that's <u>hotter</u> than its surroundings <u>emits more IR radiation</u> than it <u>absorbs</u> as it <u>cools down</u> (e.g. a cup of tea left on a table). And an object that's <u>cooler</u> than its surroundings <u>absorbs</u> more IR radiation than it <u>emits</u> as it <u>warms up</u> (e.g. a cold glass of water on a sunny day).

4) Objects at a <u>constant temperature</u> emit infrared radiation at the <u>same rate</u> that they are <u>absorbing it</u>.

5) <u>Some colours</u> and <u>surfaces absorb</u> and <u>emit</u> radiation better than others. For example, a <u>black</u> surface is <u>better</u> at absorbing and emitting radiation than a <u>white</u> one, and a <u>matt</u> surface is <u>better</u> at absorbing and emitting radiation than a <u>shiny</u> one.

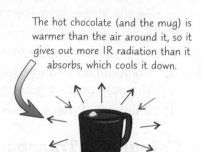

The hot chocolate (and the mug) is warmer than the air around it, so it gives out more IR radiation than it absorbs, which cools it down.

You Can Investigate Emission With a Leslie Cube

A <u>Leslie cube</u> is a <u>hollow</u>, <u>watertight</u>, metal cube made of e.g. aluminium, whose four <u>vertical faces</u> have <u>different surfaces</u> (for example, matt black paint, matt white paint, shiny metal and dull metal). You can use them to <u>investigate IR emission</u> by different surfaces:

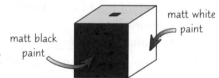

matt black paint

matt white paint

PRACTICAL

1) Place an <u>empty Leslie cube</u> on a <u>heat-proof</u> mat.

2) <u>Boil</u> water in a kettle and <u>fill</u> the Leslie cube with boiling water.

3) Wait a while for the cube to <u>warm up</u>, then hold a <u>thermometer</u> against each of the four vertical faces of the cube. You should find that all four faces are the <u>same temperature</u>.

4) Hold an <u>infrared detector</u> a <u>set distance</u> (e.g. 10 cm) away from one of the cube's vertical faces, and record the <u>amount of IR radiation</u> it detects.

5) <u>Repeat</u> this measurement for <u>each</u> of the cube's <u>vertical faces</u>. Make sure you position the detector at the <u>same distance</u> from the cube each time.

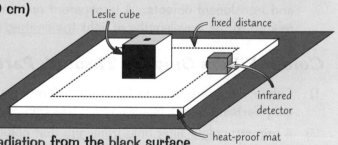

Leslie cube

fixed distance

infrared detector

heat-proof mat

6) You should find that you detect <u>more infrared radiation</u> from the <u>black</u> surface than the <u>white</u> one, and more from the <u>matt</u> surfaces than the <u>shiny</u> ones.

7) As always, you should do the experiment <u>more than once</u>, to make sure your results are <u>repeatable</u> (p.4).

8) It's important to be <u>careful</u> when you're doing this experiment. <u>Don't</u> try to <u>move the cube</u> when it's full of <u>boiling water</u> — you might burn your hands. And be careful if you're carrying a <u>full kettle</u> — your mate won't thank you if you spill boiling water into their bag (or down their back).

> You can also investigate how absorption depends on surface. One way is to stick ball bearings to the back of two different surfaces with wax and see which one falls off first when the surfaces are placed equal distances from a bunsen burner.

Feelin' hot hot hot...

Get that link between radiation and temperature firmly stuck in your head. Then have a go at this question:

Q1   Explain what is happening in terms of radiation and temperature when a bowl of ice cream is left on a counter in a warm room.

[2 marks]

Black Body Radiation

It sounds complicated, but black body radiation is not as hard as it sounds.
Just take your time and make sure you really understand what's going on in that graph.

Black Bodies are the Ultimate Emitters

1) A perfect black body is an object that absorbs all of the radiation that hits it. No radiation is reflected or transmitted.

2) All objects emit electromagnetic (EM) radiation due to the energy in their thermal energy stores. This radiation isn't just in the infrared part of the spectrum — it covers a range of wavelengths and frequencies. Perfect black bodies are the best possible emitters of radiation.

3) The intensity and distribution of the wavelengths emitted by an object depend on the object's temperature. Intensity is the power per unit area, i.e. how much energy is transferred to a given area in a certain amount of time.

4) As the temperature of an object increases, the intensity of every emitted wavelength increases.

5) However, the intensity increases more rapidly for shorter wavelengths than longer wavelengths. This causes the peak wavelength (the wavelength with the highest intensity) to decrease.

6) The curves on the right show how the intensity and wavelength distribution of a black body depends on its temperature.

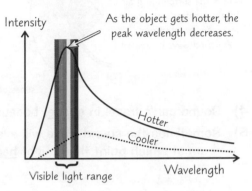

As the object gets hotter, the peak wavelength decreases.

Radiation Affects the Earth's Temperature

1) The overall temperature of the Earth depends on the amount of radiation it reflects, absorbs and emits.

2) During the day, lots of radiation (like light) is transferred to the Earth from the Sun and absorbed. This causes an increase in local temperature.

3) At night, less radiation is being absorbed than is being emitted, causing a decrease in the local temperature.

4) Overall, the temperature of the Earth stays fairly constant. You can show the flow of radiation for the Earth on a handy diagram.

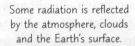

5) Changes to the atmosphere can cause a change to the Earth's overall temperature. If the atmosphere starts to absorb more radiation without emitting the same amount, the overall temperature will rise until absorption and emission are equal again (global warming).

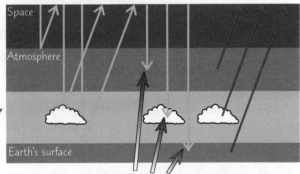

Some radiation is reflected by the atmosphere, clouds and the Earth's surface.

Radiation is also emitted.

Some radiation is absorbed by the atmosphere, clouds and the Earth's surface.

Don't let this get you hot under the collar...

The peak wavelength of radiation you emit is about 10 μm — and you thought this topic was dull...

Q1 The peak wavelength of light from the Sun is about 500 nm.
The peak wavelength of light from a second star is at about 850 nm.
Which star is hotter? Explain your answer.

[2 marks]

Sound Waves

Time to learn all about the <u>properties</u> of <u>sound waves</u> and how they cause us to <u>hear</u> things. Don't panic though — you won't be quizzed on each individual part of the <u>ear</u>, just make sure you have a general idea.

Sound Travels as a Wave

1) <u>Sound waves</u> are caused by <u>vibrating objects</u>. These vibrations are passed through the surrounding medium as a series of <u>compressions</u> and <u>rarefactions</u> (sound is a type of <u>longitudinal wave</u> — page 73).

2) Sound generally travels <u>faster in solids</u> than in liquids, and faster in liquids than in gases.

3) When a sound wave travels <u>through a solid</u> it does so by causing the <u>particles</u> in the solid to <u>vibrate</u>.

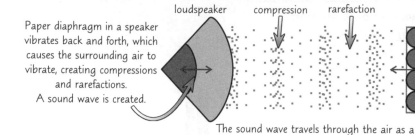

Paper diaphragm in a speaker vibrates back and forth, which causes the surrounding air to vibrate, creating compressions and rarefactions. A sound wave is created.

loudspeaker   compression   rarefaction   solid object

The sound wave travels through the air as a series of compressions and rarefactions.

When the sound wave hits a solid object, the air particles hitting the object (the pressure — p.41) causes the particles in the solid to move back and forth (vibrate).

These particles hit the next particles in line and so on — passing the sound wave through the object as a series of vibrations.

4) Sound can't travel in <u>space</u>, because it's mostly a <u>vacuum</u> (there are no particles to move or vibrate).

5) Sometimes the sound wave will eventually travel into someone's <u>ear</u> and reach their <u>ear drum</u> at which point they might <u>hear the sound</u> — more on this below.

You Hear Sound When Your Ear Drum Vibrates

outer ear   middle ear   inner ear

1) Sound waves that reach your <u>ear drum</u> can cause it to <u>vibrate</u>.

2) These <u>vibrations</u> are passed on to <u>tiny bones</u> in your ear called ossicles, through the semicircular canals and to the cochlea.

semicircular canals

auditory nerve — to the brain

ear drum

3) The <u>cochlea</u> turns these vibrations into <u>electrical signals</u> which get sent to your brain and allow you to <u>sense</u> (i.e. <u>hear</u>) the sound.

cochlea

ossicles

4) <u>Different materials</u> can convert different <u>frequencies</u> of sound waves into <u>vibrations</u>. For example, <u>humans</u> can hear sound in the range of <u>20 Hz – 20 kHz</u>. Microphones can pick up sound waves <u>outside</u> of this range, but if you tried to listen to this sound, you probably <u>wouldn't hear anything</u>.

Microphones work in a similar way. Sound waves cause a diaphragm to vibrate and this movement is transferred into an electrical signal.

5) Human hearing is limited by the <u>size</u> and <u>shape</u> of our <u>ear drum</u>, as well as the <u>structure</u> of all the parts within the ear that <u>vibrate</u> to transfer the energy from the sound wave.

Sound Waves Can Reflect and Refract

1) Sound waves will be <u>reflected</u> by <u>hard flat surfaces</u>. <u>Echoes</u> are just reflected sound waves.

2) <u>Sound waves</u> will also <u>refract</u> as they enter <u>different media</u>. As they enter <u>denser material</u>, they <u>speed up</u>. This is because when a wave travels into a different medium, its <u>wavelength changes</u> but its <u>frequency remains the same</u> so its <u>speed</u> must also <u>change</u> (p.73) (However, since sound waves are always spreading out so much, the change in direction is <u>hard to spot</u> under normal circumstances.)

Sorry, listening to music doesn't count as revision...

Make sure you know that sound waves make solids vibrate and that your vibrating ear drum lets you hear them.

Q1   Explain, in terms of vibrations, what happens when a sound wave enters your ear.   [4 marks]

Ultrasound

Can you hear <u>that</u>? If not, '<u>that</u>' could be <u>ultrasound</u> — a handy wave used for <u>seeing hidden objects</u>.

Ultrasound is Sound with Frequencies Higher Than 20 000 Hz

Electrical devices can be made which produce <u>electrical oscillations</u> over <u>a range of frequencies</u>. These can easily be converted into <u>mechanical vibrations</u> to produce <u>sound</u> waves <u>beyond the range of human hearing</u> (i.e. frequencies above 20 000 Hz). This is called <u>ultrasound</u> and it pops up all over the place.

Ultrasound Waves Get Partially Reflected at Boundaries

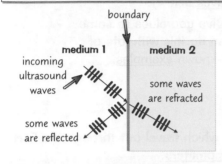

1) When a wave passes from one medium into another, <u>some</u> of the wave is <u>reflected</u> off the boundary between the two media, and some is transmitted (and refracted). This is <u>partial reflection</u>.

2) What this means is that you can point a pulse of ultrasound at an object, and wherever there are <u>boundaries</u> between one substance and another, some of the ultrasound gets <u>reflected back</u>.

3) The time it takes for the reflections to reach a <u>detector</u> can be used to measure <u>how far away</u> the boundary is.

Ultrasound is Useful in Lots of Different Ways

Medical imaging, e.g. pre-natal scanning of a foetus

1) <u>Ultrasound waves</u> can pass through the body, but whenever they reach a boundary between <u>two different media</u> (like fluid in the womb and the skin of the foetus) some of the wave is <u>reflected back</u> and <u>detected</u>.

2) The exact <u>timing and distribution</u> of these <u>echoes</u> are processed by a computer to produce a <u>video image</u> of the foetus.

3) No one knows for sure if ultrasound is safe in all cases but <u>X-rays</u> would definitely be dangerous.

ultrasound transmitter/receiver

partial reflection

foetus

Industrial imaging, e.g. finding flaws in materials

1) Ultrasound can also be used to find <u>flaws</u> in objects such as <u>pipes</u> or <u>materials</u> such as wood or metal.

2) Ultrasound waves entering a material will usually be <u>reflected</u> by the <u>far side</u> of the material.

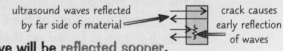

ultrasound waves reflected by far side of material

crack causes early reflection of waves

3) If there is a flaw such as a <u>crack</u> inside the object, the wave will be <u>reflected sooner</u>.

<u>Echo sounding</u> uses high frequency <u>sound waves</u> (including <u>ultrasound</u>). It's used by boats and submarines to find out the <u>depth of the water</u> they are in or to <u>locate</u> objects in <u>deep water</u>.

EXAMPLE: A pulse of ultrasound takes 4.5 seconds to travel from a submarine to the seabed and back again. If the speed of sound in seawater is 1520 m/s, how far away is the submarine from the seabed?

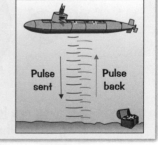

1) The formula is of course distance = speed × time $s = vt = 1520 × 4.5 = 6840$

2) But this is a reflection question, so don't forget the factor of 2. $6840 ÷ 2 = 3420$ m.

3) The 4.5 s is for there and back, so halve the distance.

Pulse sent   Pulse back

Partially reflected — completely revised...

Ultrasound waves are really useful, so make sure you can describe how looking at the time taken for them to be reflected can let you see the structure of things you would otherwise be unable to — like the inside of a metal.

Q1   Calculate how long it takes for an ultrasound pulse to return to a submarine, if the speed of sound in seawater is 1520 m/s and the submarine is 2500 m above the seabed.   [3 marks]

Exploring Structures Using Waves

Ultrasound waves can be used to explore structures that we can't see, but they're not the only ones.
E.g. you can use seismic waves produced by earthquakes to investigate the Earth's inner structure. Fancy.

Waves Can Be Used to Detect and Explore

1) Waves have different properties (e.g. speed) depending on the material they're travelling through.

2) When a wave arrives at a boundary between materials, a number of things can happen.

3) It can be completely reflected or partially reflected (like in ultrasound imaging, see previous page). The wave may continue travelling in the same direction but at a different speed, or it may be refracted (p.76) or absorbed (like S-waves below).

4) Studying the properties and paths of waves through structures can give you clues to some of the properties of the structure that you can't see by eye. You can do this with lots of different waves — ultrasound and seismic waves are two good, well-known examples.

Earthquakes and Explosions Cause Seismic Waves

1) When there's an earthquake somewhere, it produces seismic waves which travel out through the Earth. We detect these waves all over the surface of the planet using seismometers.

2) Seismologists work out the time it takes for the shock waves to reach each seismometer. They also note which parts of the Earth don't receive the shock waves at all.

3) When seismic waves reach a boundary between different layers of material (which all have different properties, like density) inside the Earth, some waves will be absorbed and some will be refracted.

4) Most of the time, if the waves are refracted they change speed gradually, resulting in a curved path. But when the properties change suddenly, the wave speed changes abruptly, and the path has a kink.

P-waves can Travel through the Earth's Core, S-waves can't

1) There are two different types of seismic waves you need to learn — P waves and S waves (see below).

2) By observing how seismic waves are absorbed and refracted, scientists have been able to work out where the properties of the Earth change dramatically. Our current understanding of the internal structure of the Earth and the size of the Earth's core is based on these observations.

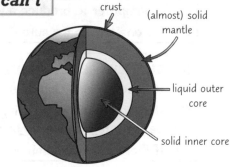

crust
(almost) solid mantle
liquid outer core
solid inner core

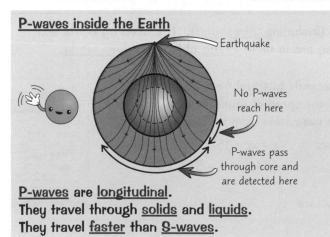

P-waves inside the Earth

Earthquake
No P-waves reach here
P-waves pass through core and are detected here

P-waves are longitudinal.
They travel through solids and liquids.
They travel faster than S-waves.

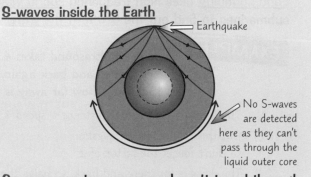

S-waves inside the Earth

Earthquake
No S-waves are detected here as they can't pass through the liquid outer core

S-waves are transverse and can't travel through liquids (or gases). They're slower than P-waves.

I'll take an Earth with metal filling and a crispy crust to go...

Wow, who knew earthquakes could be so educational as well as destructive...

Q1   S-waves produced at the Earth's North Pole would not be detected at the South Pole. Suggest one conclusion you can make about the Earth's core from the observation. Explain your answer.   [2 marks]

Revision Questions for Topic 6

And that's the end of <u>Topic 6</u> — give yourself a pat on the back before seeing <u>how much you've learnt</u>.

- Try these questions and <u>tick off each one</u> when you <u>get it right</u>.
- When you've done <u>all the questions</u> under a heading and are <u>completely happy</u> with it, tick it off.

<u>Wave Properties (p.73-74)</u> ☑

1) What is the amplitude, wavelength, frequency and period of a wave?

2) Describe the difference between transverse and longitudinal waves and give an example of each kind.

3) Describe experiments you could do to measure the speed of sound and the speed of ripples in water.

<u>Reflection and Refraction (p.75-77)</u> ☑

4) State the law of reflection.

5) Draw a ray diagram for a light ray being reflected where the angle of incidence is 25°.

6) Define specular and diffuse reflection.

7) True or false? All electromagnetic waves are transverse.

8) Explain refraction and draw a ray diagram for a light ray entering a less optically dense material.

9) Describe an experiment you could do to investigate a) refraction and b) reflection of light.

<u>Uses and Dangers of Electromagnetic Waves (p.78-81)</u> ☑

10) What kind of current is used to generate radio waves in an antenna?

11) Explain why microwaves are used for satellite communication and mobile phone signals.

12) Give an everyday use of infrared radiation.

13) What type of radiation is used to transmit a signal in an optical fibre?

14) Name the type of radiation produced by the lamps in tanning salons.

15) What does the term 'ionising radiation' mean?

16) What does radiation dose in sieverts measure?

<u>Lenses (p.82-84)</u> ☑

17) Give the three rules for refraction in a convex lens and the three for a concave lens.

18) Explain the terms 'real image' and 'virtual image'.

19) Draw the ray diagram symbols for a converging lens and a diverging lens.

<u>Visible Light and Black Body Radiation (p.85-87)</u> ☑

20) True or false? Opaque objects transmit light.

21) Describe how colour filters work.

22) Describe the rates of radiation absorption and emission for an object at a constant temperature.

23) What is a perfect black body?

24) What is a Leslie cube? How could you use one to investigate IR emission by different surfaces?

25) a) Draw a diagram showing radiation reflected, absorbed and emitted by the Earth and its atmosphere.
    b) Explain how this absorption, reflection and emission of radiation affects the Earth's temperature.

<u>Sound Waves and Exploring Structures with Waves (p.88-90)</u> ☑

26) What is the frequency range of human hearing?

27) Explain how ultrasound is used in pre-natal scanning, industry and echo sounding.

28) Describe how S and P waves can be used to explore the structure of the Earth's core.

Permanent and Induced Magnets

I think magnetism is an <u>attractive</u> subject, but don't get <u>repelled</u> by the exam — <u>revise</u>.

Magnets Produce Magnetic Fields

1) All magnets have <u>two poles</u> — <u>north</u> (or north seeking) and <u>south</u> (or south seeking).

2) All magnets produce a <u>magnetic field</u> — a region where <u>other magnets</u> or <u>magnetic materials</u> (e.g. iron, steel, nickel and cobalt) experience a <u>force</u>. (This is a <u>non-contact force</u> — similar to the force on charges in an electric field, like you saw on page 36.)

3) You can show a magnetic field by drawing <u>magnetic field lines</u>.

4) The lines always go from <u>north to south</u> and they show <u>which way</u> a force would act on a north pole if it was put at that point in the field.

5) The <u>closer together</u> the lines are, the <u>stronger</u> the magnetic field. The <u>further away</u> from a magnet you get, the <u>weaker</u> the field is.

6) The magnetic field is <u>strongest</u> at the <u>poles</u> of a magnet. This means that the <u>magnetic forces</u> are also <u>strongest</u> at the poles.

7) The force between a <u>magnet</u> and a <u>magnetic material</u> is <u>always attractive</u>, no matter the pole.

8) If <u>two poles</u> of a magnet are put <u>near</u> each other, they will each exert a <u>force</u> on each other. This force can be <u>attractive</u> or <u>repulsive</u>. Two poles that are the same (these are called <u>like poles</u>) will <u>repel</u> each other. Two <u>unlike</u> poles will <u>attract</u> each other.

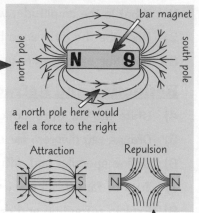

bar magnet

north pole   south pole

a north pole here would feel a force to the right

Attraction   Repulsion

Compasses Show the Directions of Magnetic Fields

1) Inside a compass is a tiny <u>bar magnet</u>. The <u>north</u> pole of this magnet is attracted to the south pole of any other magnet it is near. So the compass <u>points</u> in the direction of the magnetic field it is in.

2) You can move a compass around a magnet and <u>trace</u> its position on some paper to build up a picture of what the magnetic field <u>looks like</u>.

3) When they're not near a magnet, compasses always point <u>north</u>. This is because the <u>Earth</u> generates its own <u>magnetic field</u>, which shows the <u>inside</u> (<u>core</u>) of the Earth must be <u>magnetic</u>.

The north pole of the magnet in the compass points along the field line towards the south pole of the bar magnet.

NORTH POLE

Magnets Can be Permanent or Induced

1) There are <u>two types</u> of magnet — <u>permanent</u> magnets and <u>induced</u> magnets.

2) <u>Permanent</u> magnets produce their <u>own</u> magnetic field.

3) <u>Induced</u> magnets are magnetic materials that <u>turn into</u> a magnet when they're put into a magnetic field.

4) The force between permanent and induced magnets is always <u>attractive</u> (see magnetic materials above).

5) When you <u>take away</u> the magnetic field, induced magnets quickly <u>lose their magnetism</u> (or most of it) and <u>stop producing</u> a magnetic field.

N permanent magnet S   magnetic material

The magnetic material becomes magnetised when it is brought near the bar magnet. It has its own poles and magnetic field:

N permanent magnet S   N induced magnet S

induced poles

Magnets are like farmers — surrounded by fields...

Magnetism is one of those things that takes a while to make much sense. Learn these basics — you'll need them.

Q1   Draw the magnetic field lines for a bar magnet. Label the areas where the field is strongest.   [2 marks]

Q2   Give two differences between permanent and induced magnets.   [2 marks]

Electromagnetism

On this page you'll see that a <u>magnetic field</u> is also found around a <u>wire</u> that has a <u>current</u> passing through it.

A Moving Charge Creates a Magnetic Field

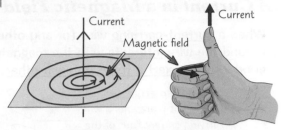

The Right-Hand Thumb Rule
Using your right hand, point your thumb in the direction of current and curl your fingers. The direction of your fingers is the direction of the field.

1) When a <u>current flows</u> through a <u>wire</u>, a <u>magnetic field</u> is created <u>around</u> the wire.

2) The field is made up of <u>concentric circles</u> perpendicular to the wire, with the wire in the centre.

3) You can see this by placing a <u>compass</u> near a <u>wire</u> that is carrying a <u>current</u>. As you move the compass, it will <u>trace</u> the direction of the magnetic field.

4) Changing the <u>direction</u> of the <u>current</u> changes the direction of the <u>magnetic field</u> — use the <u>right-hand thumb rule</u> to work out which way it goes.

5) The <u>strength</u> of the magnetic field produced <u>changes</u> with the <u>current</u> and the <u>distance</u> from the wire. The <u>larger</u> the current through the wire, or the <u>closer</u> to the wire you are, the <u>stronger</u> the field is.

A Solenoid is a Coil of Wire

1) You can <u>increase</u> the <u>strength</u> of the magnetic field that a wire produces by <u>wrapping</u> the wire into a <u>coil</u> called a <u>solenoid</u>.

2) This happens because the field lines around each loop of wire <u>line up</u> with each other.

3) This results in <u>lots</u> of field lines <u>pointing in the same direction</u> that are <u>very close</u> to each other. As you saw on the last page, the closer together field lines are, the <u>stronger</u> the field is.

4) The magnetic field <u>inside</u> a solenoid is <u>strong</u> and <u>uniform</u> (it has the <u>same strength</u> and <u>direction</u> at every point in that region).

5) <u>Outside</u> the coil, the magnetic field is just like the one round a <u>bar magnet</u>.

6) You can <u>increase</u> the field strength of the solenoid <u>even more</u> by putting a block of <u>iron</u> in the <u>centre</u> of the coil. This <u>iron core</u> becomes an <u>induced</u> magnet whenever current is flowing.

7) If you <u>stop</u> the current, the magnetic field <u>disappears</u>. A <u>solenoid with an iron core</u> (a magnet whose magnetic field can be turned <u>on</u> and <u>off</u> with an <u>electric current</u>) is called an **ELECTROMAGNET**.

Electromagnets Have Lots of Uses

Magnets you can switch on and off are really <u>useful</u>. They're usually used because they're so <u>quick</u> to turn on and off or because they can create a <u>varying force</u> (like in <u>loudspeakers</u>, p.95).

1) Electromagnets are used in some cranes to <u>attract</u> and <u>pick up</u> things made from magnetic materials like iron and steel, e.g. in <u>scrap yards</u>. Using an electromagnet means the magnet can be switched <u>on</u> when you want to <u>pick stuff up</u>, then switched <u>off</u> when you want to <u>drop</u> it.

2) Electromagnets can also be used <u>within other circuits</u> to act as switches (e.g. in the electric starters of motors), like this:

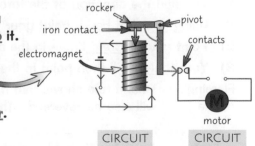

- When the switch in circuit one is <u>closed</u>, it turns on the <u>electromagnet</u>, which <u>attracts</u> the <u>iron contact</u> on the <u>rocker</u>.

- The rocker <u>pivots</u> and <u>closes the contacts</u>, completing circuit two, and <u>turning on the motor</u>.

Strong, in uniform and a magnetic personality — I'm a catch...

Electromagnets are used in loads of everyday things from alarms to trains, so you'd better learn how they work.

Q1   Draw the magnetic field for: a) a current-carrying wire   b) a current-carrying solenoid   [4 marks]

The Motor Effect

The <u>motor effect</u> can happen when you put a <u>current-carrying wire</u> in a <u>magnetic field</u>. It's really useful in stuff like... well... electric motors. If you want to know exactly what it is, you'll have to <u>keep reading</u>.

A Current in a Magnetic Field Experiences a Force

When a <u>current-carrying</u> wire (or any other <u>conductor</u>) is put between magnetic poles, the <u>magnetic field</u> around the wire <u>interacts</u> with the magnetic field it has been placed in. This causes the magnet and the conductor to <u>exert a force on each other</u>. This is called the <u>motor effect</u> and can cause the <u>wire</u> to <u>move</u>.

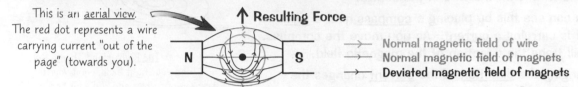

This is an <u>aerial view</u>.
The red dot represents a wire carrying current "out of the page" (towards you).

↑ Resulting Force

→ Normal magnetic field of wire
→ Normal magnetic field of magnets
→ Deviated magnetic field of magnets

1) To experience the <u>full force</u>, the <u>wire</u> has to be at <u>90°</u> to the <u>magnetic field</u>. If the wire runs <u>parallel</u> to the <u>magnetic field</u>, it won't experience <u>any force at all</u>. At angles in between, it'll feel <u>some</u> force.

2) The force always acts at <u>right angles</u> to the <u>magnetic field</u> of the magnets and the <u>direction of the current</u> in the wire.

3) A good way of showing the direction of the force is to apply a current to a set of <u>rails</u> inside a <u>horseshoe magnet</u> (shown opposite). A bar is placed on the rails, which <u>completes the circuit</u>. This generates a <u>force</u> that <u>rolls the bar</u> along the rails.

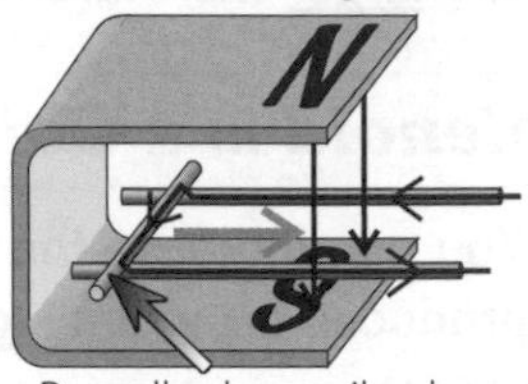

Horseshoe magnet

Bar rolls along rails when current is applied

4) The magnitude (strength) of the force <u>increases</u> with the <u>strength</u> of the <u>magnetic field</u>.

5) The force also <u>increases</u> with the amount of <u>current</u> passing through the conductor.

You Can Find the Size of the Force...

The <u>force</u> acting on a <u>conductor</u> in a <u>magnetic field</u> depends on three things:

1) The <u>magnetic flux density</u> — how many <u>field</u> (<u>flux</u>) lines there are in a <u>region</u>. This shows the <u>strength</u> of the magnetic field (p.92).

2) The size of the <u>current</u> through the conductor.

3) The <u>length</u> of the conductor that's <u>in</u> the magnetic field.

When the current is at <u>90°</u> to the magnetic field it is in, the <u>force</u> acting on it can be found using the equation on the right.

Force (N) — $F = BIl$ — Current (A), Length (m)

Magnetic flux density (T, tesla)

... and Which Way it's Acting

You can find the direction of the force with <u>Fleming's left-hand rule</u>.

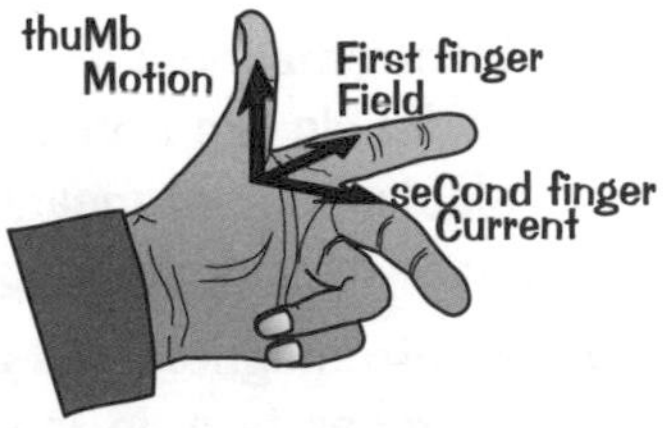

1) Using your <u>left hand</u>, point your <u>First finger</u> in the direction of the <u>Field</u>.

2) Point your <u>seCond finger</u> in the direction of the <u>Current</u>.

3) Your <u>thuMb</u> will then point in the direction of the <u>force</u> (Motion).

thuMb Motion
First finger Field
seCond finger Current

Fleming's left-hand rule shows that if either the <u>current</u> or the <u>magnetic field</u> is <u>reversed</u>, then the direction of the <u>force</u> will also be reversed. This can be used for all sorts of things — like <u>motors</u> on the next page.

Left-hand rule for the motor effect — drive on the left...

Use the left-hand rule in the exam. You might look a bit silly, but it makes getting those marks so much easier.

Q1 A 20 cm section of wire with a current of 8 A is at 90° to a 0.1 T magnetic field.

a) Find the direction of the force acting on the wire. [1 mark]

b) Calculate the size of the force. [3 marks]

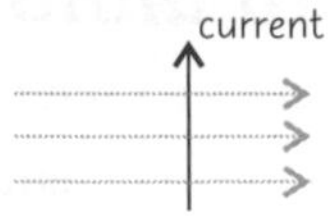

current

magnetic field

Electric Motors and Loudspeakers

If you've ever broken a pair of headphones, you'll have seen the tiny crinkly <u>paper cone</u> inside them. I'm sure you've never sat and wondered <u>how they work</u>, but that's all about to change my friend...

A Current-Carrying Coil of Wire Rotates in a Magnetic Field

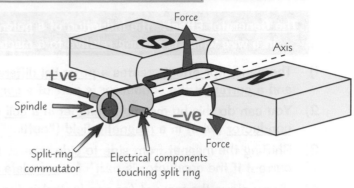

1) The diagram on the right shows a <u>basic dc motor</u>. <u>Forces</u> act on the two <u>side arms</u> of a <u>coil</u> of wire that's carrying a <u>current</u>.

2) These forces are just the <u>usual forces</u> which act on <u>any current</u> in a <u>magnetic field</u> (p.94).

3) Because the coil is on a <u>spindle</u> and the forces act <u>one up</u> and <u>one down</u>, it <u>rotates</u>.

4) The <u>split-ring commutator</u> is a clever way of <u>swapping</u> the contacts <u>every half turn</u> to keep the motor rotating in the <u>same direction</u>.

5) The direction of the motor can be <u>reversed</u> either by swapping the <u>polarity</u> of the <u>dc supply</u> (reversing the <u>current</u>) or swapping the <u>magnetic poles</u> over (reversing the <u>field</u>).

6) You can use <u>Fleming's left-hand rule</u> to work out which way the coil will <u>turn</u>.

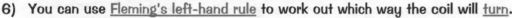

EXAMPLE: Is the coil turning clockwise or anticlockwise?

1) Draw in <u>current arrows</u> (from positive to negative, p.24).
2) Use <u>Fleming's left-hand rule</u> on <u>one</u> branch (here, I've picked the right-hand branch).
3) Point your <u>first finger</u> in the direction of the magnetic <u>field</u> (remember, this is <u>north to south</u>).
4) Point your <u>second</u> finger in the direction of the <u>current</u>.
5) Draw in the <u>direction of motion</u> (the direction your <u>thumb</u> is pointing in).

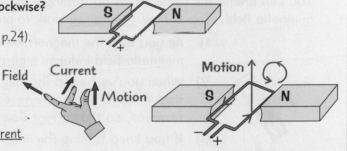

The coil is turning anticlockwise.

Loudspeakers Work Because of the Motor Effect

<u>Loudspeakers</u> and <u>headphones</u> (which are just tiny loudspeakers) both use <u>electromagnets</u>:

1) An <u>alternating current</u> (ac) is sent through a coil of wire attached to the <u>base of a paper cone</u>.

2) The coil <u>surrounds one pole</u> of a <u>permanent magnet</u>, and is <u>surrounded by the other</u> pole, so the current causes a <u>force</u> on the coil (which causes the cone to <u>move</u>).

3) When the current <u>reverses</u>, the force acts in the <u>opposite direction</u>, which causes the cone to move in the opposite direction too.

4) So <u>variations</u> in the <u>current</u> make the cone <u>vibrate</u>, which makes the air around the cone vibrate and creates the variations in <u>pressure</u> that cause a <u>sound wave</u> (p.88).

5) The <u>frequency</u> of the <u>sound wave</u> is the <u>same</u> as the frequency of the ac, so by controlling the frequency of the ac you can <u>alter the sound wave</u> produced.

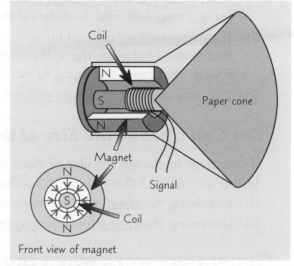

If a loudspeaker falls in the forest does it still make a sound...

Motors and speakers are both really common examples, so make sure you learn them well for the exam.

Q1 Explain how a loudspeaker converts electrical signals into sound waves. [4 marks]

The Generator Effect

Electricity is generated using the <u>generator effect</u> (which is also known as <u>electromagnetic induction</u>). Sounds terrifying, but read this page carefully and it hopefully shouldn't be too complicated.

Cutting Field Lines Induces a Potential Difference

> **The Generator Effect:** The <u>induction</u> of a <u>potential difference</u> (and <u>current</u> if there's a <u>complete circuit</u>) in a wire which is <u>moving relative</u> to a <u>magnetic field</u>, or experiencing a <u>change in magnetic field</u>.

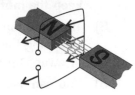

1) The <u>generator effect</u> creates a <u>potential difference</u> in a conductor, and a <u>current</u> if the conductor is part of a <u>complete circuit</u>.

2) You can do this by moving a <u>magnet</u> in a <u>coil of wire</u> OR moving a <u>conductor</u> (wire) in a <u>magnetic field</u> ("cutting" magnetic field lines).

3) Shifting the magnet from <u>side to side</u> creates a little "blip" of current if the conductor is part of a <u>complete circuit</u>.

4) If you move the magnet (or conductor) in the <u>opposite direction</u>, then the potential difference/current will be <u>reversed</u>. Likewise if the <u>polarity</u> of the magnet is <u>reversed</u>, then the potential difference/current will be <u>reversed</u> too.

5) If you keep the magnet (or the coil) moving <u>backwards and forwards</u>, you produce a potential difference that keeps swapping direction — an <u>alternating current</u>.

You can create the same effect by turning a magnet <u>end to end</u> in a coil, or turning a coil inside a magnetic field. This is how <u>generators</u> work to produce <u>ac</u> or <u>direct current</u> (<u>dc</u>) — see next page.

side view

coil

1) As you turn the magnet, the magnetic field through the coil <u>changes</u>. This change in the magnetic field induces a <u>potential difference</u>, which can make a <u>current</u> flow in the wire.

2) When you've turned the magnet through half a turn, the <u>direction</u> of the magnetic field through the coil <u>reverses</u>. When this happens, the potential difference reverses, so the <u>current</u> flows in the <u>opposite direction</u> around the coil of wire.

3) If you keep turning the magnet in the <u>same direction</u> — always clockwise, say — then the potential difference will keep on reversing every half turn and you'll get an <u>alternating current</u>.

Induced Current Opposes the Change that Made It

1) So, a change in magnetic field can <u>induce a current</u> in a wire. But, as you saw on page 93, when a current flows through a wire, a <u>magnetic field</u> is created <u>around</u> the wire. (Yep, that's a <u>second</u> magnetic field — different to the one whose field lines were being cut in the first place.)

2) The <u>magnetic field</u> created by an <u>induced</u> current always acts <u>against the change</u> that made it (whether that's the movement of a wire or a change in the field it's in). Basically, it's trying to return things to <u>the way they were</u>.

3) This means that the <u>induced current</u> always <u>opposes</u> the change that made it.

You Can Change the Size of the Induced Potential Difference

If you want to change the <u>size</u> of the induced pd, you have to change the <u>rate</u> that the <u>magnetic field</u> is changing. Induced <u>potential difference</u> (and so <u>induced current</u>) can be <u>increased</u> by either:

1) Increasing the <u>speed</u> of the movement — cutting <u>more</u> magnetic field lines in a given <u>time</u>.

2) Increasing the <u>strength</u> of the <u>magnetic field</u> (so there are more field lines that can be cut).

Generators work when the coil or the field is moving...

Electricity is super useful in our daily lives, which means the generator effect is really important too. Learn it.

Q1   State the generator effect.   [1 mark]

Q2   Give two ways to increase the induced current in a generator.   [2 marks]

Generators and Microphones

Generators make use of the generator effect from the previous page to induce a current. Whether this current is alternating or direct all depends on two similar sounding methods of connection. Don't get them mixed up.

Alternators Generate Alternating Current

1) Generators rotate a coil in a magnetic field (or a magnet in a coil).

2) Their construction is pretty much like a motor.

3) As the coil (or magnet) spins, a current is induced in the coil. This current changes direction every half turn.

4) Instead of a split-ring commutator, ac generators have slip rings and brushes so the contacts don't swap every half turn.

5) This means they produce an alternating potential difference — more on this below.

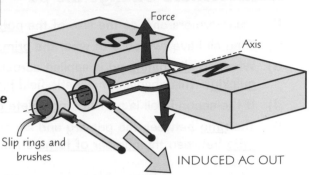

Dynamos Generate Direct Current

1) Dynamos work in the same way as alternators, apart from one important difference.

2) They have a split-ring commutator instead of slip rings.

3) This swaps the connection every half turn to keep the current flowing in the same direction (similar to the motion of a dc motor, p.95).

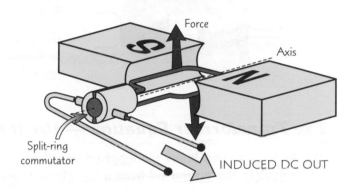

You Can Use an Oscilloscope To See the Generated pd

1) Oscilloscopes show how the potential difference generated in the coil changes over time.

2) For ac this is a line that goes up and down, crossing the horizontal axis.

3) For dc the line isn't straight like you might expect, but it stays above the axis (pd is always positive) so it's still direct current.

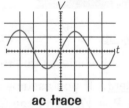 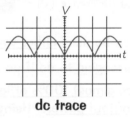

ac trace   dc trace   Increasing revolutions

4) The height of the line at a given point is the generated potential difference at that time.

5) Increasing the frequency of revolutions increases the overall pd, but it also creates more peaks too.

Microphones Generate Current From Sound Waves

1) Microphones are basically loudspeakers in reverse.

2) Sound waves hit a flexible diaphragm that is attached to a coil of wire, wrapped around a magnet.

3) This causes the coil of wire to move in the magnetic field, which generates a current.

4) The movement of the coil (and so the generated current) depends on the properties of the sound wave (louder sounds make the diaphragm move further).

5) This is how microphones can convert the pressure variations of a sound wave into variations in current in an electric circuit.

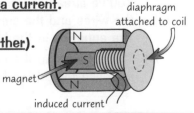

diaphragm attached to coil

magnet

induced current

---

ac from Alternators, dc from Dynamos — easy peasy...

Remember, microphones act like a loudspeaker in reverse. If you're not sure about speakers, go back to page 95.

Q1 a) Draw a potential difference-time graph for a direct current generated by a dynamo. [2 marks]
    b) Explain how the dynamo generates this current. [3 marks]

Transformers

Transformers only work with an alternating current. Try it with a battery (dc) and you'll be there for days.

Transformers Change the pd — but Only for Alternating Current

1) Transformers change the size of the potential difference of an alternating current.

2) They all have two coils of wire, the primary and the secondary, joined with an iron core.

3) When an alternating pd is applied across the primary coil, the iron core magnetises and demagnetises quickly. This changing magnetic field induces an alternating pd in the secondary coil (p.96).

4) If the second coil is part of a complete circuit, this causes a current to be induced.

5) The ratio between the primary and secondary potential differences is the same as the ratio between the number of turns on the primary and secondary coils.

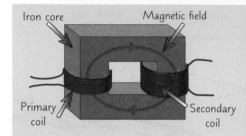

Iron core   Magnetic field

Primary coil

Secondary coil

Iron is used because it's easily magnetised.

STEP-UP TRANSFORMERS step the potential difference up (i.e. increase it). They have more turns on the secondary coil than the primary coil.

STEP-DOWN TRANSFORMERS step the potential difference down (i.e. decrease it). They have more turns on the primary coil than the secondary.

The Transformer Equation — Use it Either Way Up

1) As long as you know the input pd and the number of turns on each coil, you can calculate the output pd from a transformer using the transformer equation:

Input potential difference (V)

Output potential difference (V)

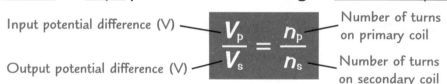

$$\frac{V_p}{V_s} = \frac{n_p}{n_s}$$

Number of turns on primary coil

Number of turns on secondary coil

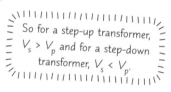

So for a step-up transformer, $V_s > V_p$ and for a step-down transformer, $V_s < V_p$.

2) This equation can be used either way up, so $\frac{V_s}{V_p} = \frac{n_s}{n_p}$ works just as well.

There's less rearranging to do if you put whatever you're trying to find (the unknown) on the top.

3) Transformers are almost 100% efficient. If you assume that they are, then the input power is equal to the output power. Using $P = VI$ from page 33, you can write this as:

Pd across secondary coil (V)

Current through secondary coil (A)

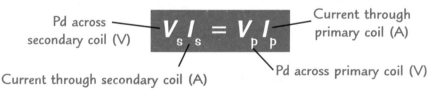

$$V_s I_s = V_p I_p$$

Current through primary coil (A)

Pd across primary coil (V)

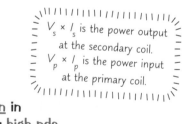

$V_s \times I_s$ is the power output at the secondary coil. $V_p \times I_p$ is the power input at the primary coil.

4) You need to be able to relate both of these equations to power transmission in the national grid, to explain why and how the national grid transmits at very high pds.

5) You've already seen on page 34 that a low current means that less energy is wasted heating the wires and the surroundings, making the national grid an efficient way of transmitting power. The equation in the blue box shows why, for a given power, a high pd is needed for a low current.

6) The equation in the orange box above can be used to work out the number of turns needed to increase the pd (and decrease the current) to the right levels.

I once had a dream about transforming into a hamster...

Make sure you know how transformers work and then take a stab at using those equations with this question.

Q1   a) A transformer has 16 turns on its primary coil, 4 turns on its secondary coil and an output potential difference of 20 V. Calculate the potential difference across the primary coil. [3 marks]

b) Calculate the input current needed to produce an output power of 320 W. [3 marks]

Topic 7 — Magnetism and Electromagnetism

Revision Questions for Topic 7

Whew, the end of Topic 7 — time to put yourself to the test and see how much you can remember.

- Try these questions and tick off each one when you get it right.
- When you've done all the questions under a heading and are completely happy with it, tick it off.

Magnetism and Basic Electromagnetism (p.92-93) ☑

1) What is a magnetic field?
2) Give three magnetic materials.
3) In what direction do magnetic field lines point?
4) Describe how you could use a compass to show the direction of a bar magnet's magnetic field lines.
5) Describe the behaviour of a compass that is far away from a magnet.
6) True or false? The force between a magnet and a magnetic material is always repulsive.
7) What happens to an induced magnet when it is moved far away from a permanent magnet?
8) Describe the magnetic field around a current-carrying wire.
9) Why does adding more turns to a solenoid increase the strength of its magnetic field?
10) Describe an electromagnet and give one example of where it could be used.

The Motor Effect (p.94-95) ☑

11) Explain why a current-carrying conductor in a magnetic field experiences a force.
12) State the equation for calculating the size of this force.
13) Name three ways you could increase the force on a current-carrying wire in a magnetic field.
14) What is Fleming's left-hand rule?
15) Explain how a basic dc motor works.
16) Draw the magnetic field for the magnet inside a loudspeaker.

The Generator Effect (p.96-97) ☑

17) Describe how you can induce a current.
18) Give two ways you could reverse the direction of an induced current.
19) True or false? Induced currents create magnetic fields that oppose the change that made them.
20) Give two ways that you can increase the size of an induced potential difference.
21) Which type of generator uses slip rings and brushes?
22) What kind of current do dynamos produce?
23) Draw a graph of potential difference against time for an ac supply.
24) Explain how microphones translate sound waves into electrical signals.

Transformers (p.98) ☑

25) What kind of current are transformers used with?
26) Why do transformers have a core of iron?
27) True or false? Step-down transformers have more coils on their primary coil than on their secondary.
28) A transformer has an input pd of 100 V and an output pd of 20 V. What kind of transformer is it?
29) State the transformer equation.
30) Write down the equation that relates the input and output currents and pds of transformers. What does this equation assume?
31) Explain how transformers are used to improve efficiency when transmitting electricity.

The Life Cycle of Stars

Stars go through <u>many traumatic stages</u> in their lives — just like teenagers.

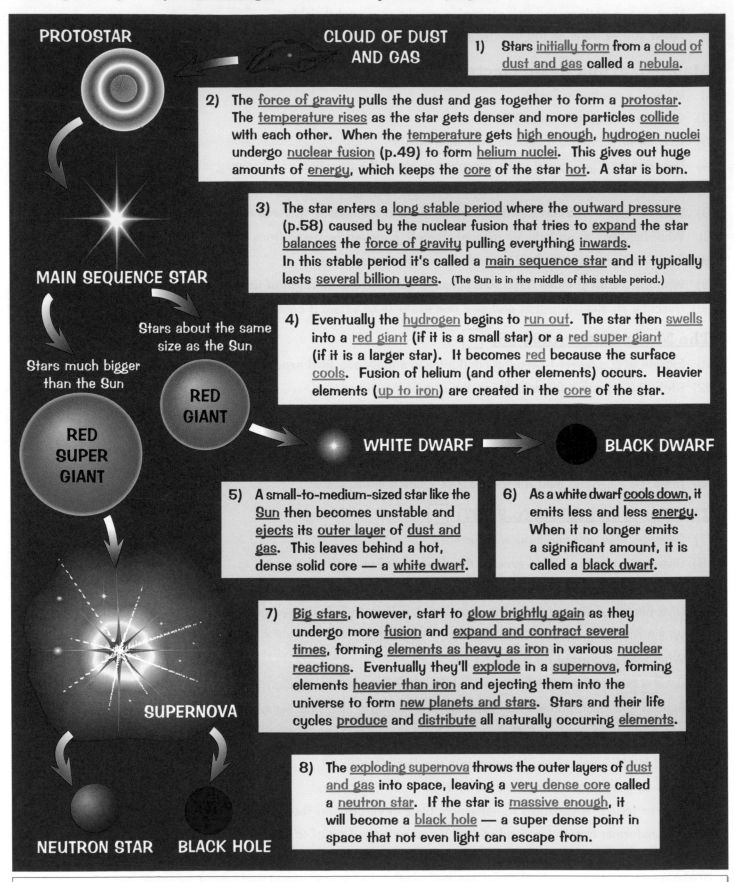

PROTOSTAR

CLOUD OF DUST AND GAS

1) Stars <u>initially form</u> from a <u>cloud of dust and gas</u> called a <u>nebula</u>.

2) The <u>force of gravity</u> pulls the dust and gas together to form a <u>protostar</u>. The <u>temperature rises</u> as the star gets denser and more particles <u>collide</u> with each other. When the <u>temperature</u> gets <u>high enough</u>, <u>hydrogen nuclei</u> undergo <u>nuclear fusion</u> (p.49) to form <u>helium nuclei</u>. This gives out huge amounts of <u>energy</u>, which keeps the <u>core</u> of the star <u>hot</u>. A star is born.

3) The star enters a <u>long stable period</u> where the <u>outward pressure</u> (p.58) caused by the nuclear fusion that tries to <u>expand</u> the star <u>balances</u> the <u>force of gravity</u> pulling everything <u>inwards</u>. In this stable period it's called a <u>main sequence star</u> and it typically lasts <u>several billion years</u>.   (The Sun is in the middle of this stable period.)

MAIN SEQUENCE STAR

Stars about the same size as the Sun

Stars much bigger than the Sun

4) Eventually the <u>hydrogen</u> begins to <u>run out</u>. The star then <u>swells</u> into a <u>red giant</u> (if it is a small star) or a <u>red super giant</u> (if it is a larger star). It becomes <u>red</u> because the surface <u>cools</u>. Fusion of helium (and other elements) occurs. Heavier elements (<u>up to iron</u>) are created in the <u>core</u> of the star.

RED GIANT

RED SUPER GIANT

WHITE DWARF   **BLACK DWARF**

5) A small-to-medium-sized star like the <u>Sun</u> then becomes unstable and <u>ejects</u> its <u>outer layer</u> of <u>dust and gas</u>. This leaves behind a hot, dense solid core — a <u>white dwarf</u>.

6) As a white dwarf <u>cools down</u>, it emits less and less <u>energy</u>. When it no longer emits a significant amount, it is called a <u>black dwarf</u>.

7) <u>Big stars</u>, however, start to <u>glow brightly again</u> as they undergo more <u>fusion</u> and <u>expand and contract several times</u>, forming <u>elements as heavy as iron</u> in various <u>nuclear reactions</u>. Eventually they'll <u>explode</u> in a <u>supernova</u>, forming elements <u>heavier than iron</u> and ejecting them into the universe to form <u>new planets and stars</u>. Stars and their life cycles <u>produce</u> and <u>distribute</u> all naturally occurring <u>elements</u>.

SUPERNOVA

8) The <u>exploding supernova</u> throws the outer layers of <u>dust and gas</u> into space, leaving a <u>very dense core</u> called a <u>neutron star</u>. If the star is <u>massive enough</u>, it will become a <u>black hole</u> — a super dense point in space that not even light can escape from.

NEUTRON STAR   BLACK HOLE

It's the beginning of the world as we know it...

Pretty neat, seeing how stars like our Sun — which all of us rely on — were made all those years ago.

Q1   Describe the life cycle of a star much larger than our Sun, from its main sequence onwards.   [4 marks]

The Solar System and Orbits

The <u>Sun</u> is the centre of our <u>solar system</u>. It's <u>orbited</u> by <u>eight planets</u>, along with a bunch of other objects.

Our Solar System has One Star — The Sun

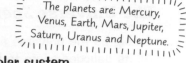

The planets are: Mercury, Venus, Earth, Mars, Jupiter, Saturn, Uranus and Neptune.

The <u>solar system</u> is all the <u>stuff</u> that <u>orbits our Sun</u>. This includes things like:

1) <u>Planets</u> — these are large objects that <u>orbit a star</u>. There are <u>eight</u> in our solar system. They have to be large enough to have "<u>cleared their neighbourhoods</u>". This means that their gravity is strong enough to have <u>pulled in</u> any nearby objects apart from their <u>natural satellites</u>.

2) <u>Dwarf planets</u>, like our pal Pluto. These are planet-like objects that orbit stars, but don't meet all of the rules for being a planet.

3) <u>Moons</u> — these orbit <u>planets</u>. They're a type of <u>natural satellite</u> (i.e. they're not man-made).

4) <u>Artificial satellites</u> are satellites that humans have built. They generally orbit the <u>Earth</u>.

Our solar system is a tiny part of the <u>Milky Way galaxy</u>. This is a <u>massive</u> collection of <u>billions</u> of stars that are all held together by gravity.

You are here.

Gravity Provides the Force That Creates Orbits

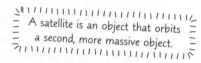

A satellite is an object that orbits a second, more massive object.

1) The planets move around the Sun in <u>almost circular</u> orbits (the same goes for the <u>Moon</u> orbiting the <u>Earth</u>).

2) If an object is <u>travelling in a circle</u> it is <u>constantly changing direction</u>, which means it is <u>constantly accelerating</u>. (Just like a car going around a roundabout, pages 60-61.)

3) This also means it is <u>constantly changing velocity</u> (but <u>NOT</u> changing <u>speed</u>).

4) For an object to accelerate, there <u>must</u> be a <u>force</u> acting on it (p.64). This force is directed towards the <u>centre</u> of the circle.

5) This force would cause the object to just <u>fall</u> towards whatever it was orbiting, but as the object is <u>already moving</u>, it just causes it to <u>change its direction</u>.

6) The object <u>keeps accelerating</u> towards what it's orbiting but the <u>instantaneous velocity</u> (which is at a <u>right angle</u> to the <u>acceleration</u>) keeps it travelling in a <u>circle</u>.

7) The force that makes this happen is provided by the <u>gravitational force</u> (gravity) between the <u>planet</u> and the <u>Sun</u> (or between the <u>planet</u> and its <u>satellites</u>).

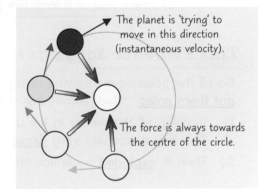

The planet is 'trying' to move in this direction (instantaneous velocity).

The force is always towards the centre of the circle.

The Size of the Orbit Depends on the Object's Speed

1) The <u>closer</u> you get to a star or planet, the <u>stronger</u> the <u>gravitational force</u> is.

2) The <u>stronger</u> the force, the <u>faster</u> the orbiting object needs to travel to remain in <u>orbit</u> (to not crash into the object that it's orbiting).

3) For an object in a <u>stable orbit</u>, if the <u>speed</u> of the object <u>changes</u>, the <u>size</u> (<u>radius</u>) of its <u>orbit</u> must do so too. <u>Faster</u> moving objects will move in a <u>stable</u> orbit with a <u>smaller radius</u> than <u>slower</u> moving ones.

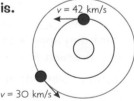

v = 42 km/s

v = 30 km/s

Revision's hard work — you've got to plan et...

Make sure you know what orbits what and how to tell a moon from a planet. Then have a go at these questions.

Q1   Give one difference between natural and artificial satellites.   [1 mark]

Q2   If the distance between the Moon and the Earth was smaller, how would the orbital speed of the Moon compare to its current orbital speed? Explain your answer.   [4 marks]

Red-shift and the Big Bang

'How it all began' is a tricky question that we just can't answer. Our <u>best guess</u> at the minute is the <u>Big Bang</u>.

The Universe Seems to Be Expanding

As big as the universe already is, it looks like it's getting even <u>bigger</u>.
All its <u>galaxies</u> seem to be <u>moving away</u> from each other. There's good evidence for this...

1) When we look at <u>light from most distant galaxies</u>, we find that the <u>wavelength</u> has increased.

2) The wavelengths are all <u>longer</u> than they should be — they're <u>shifted</u> towards the <u>red end</u> of the spectrum. This is called <u>red-shift</u>.

> You can think of the light wave 'stretching out' as the source moves away from us.

3) This suggests the <u>source</u> of the light is <u>moving away</u> from us. <u>Measurements</u> of the red-shift indicate that these <u>distant galaxies</u> are <u>moving away from us</u> (receding) very quickly — and it's the <u>same result</u> whichever direction you look in.

4) <u>More distant</u> galaxies have <u>greater</u> red-shifts than nearer ones. This means that more distant galaxies are <u>moving away faster</u> than nearer ones.

5) The inescapable <u>conclusion</u> appears to be that the whole universe (space itself) is <u>expanding</u>.

Imagine a <u>balloon</u> covered with <u>pompoms</u>.
As you <u>blow</u> into the balloon, it <u>stretches</u>.
The pompoms move <u>further away</u> from each other.

The balloon represents the <u>universe</u> and each pompom is a <u>galaxy</u>. As time goes on, <u>space stretches</u> and expands, moving the galaxies away from each other.

This is a <u>simple model</u> (balloons only stretch <u>so far</u>, and there would be galaxies '<u>inside</u>' the balloon too) but it shows how the <u>expansion</u> of space makes it look like galaxies are <u>moving away</u> from us.

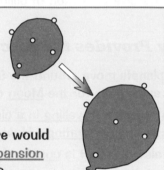

This Evidence Suggests the Universe Started with a Bang

So all the galaxies are moving away from each other at great speed — suggesting something must have <u>got them going</u>. That 'something' was probably a <u>big explosion</u> — the <u>Big Bang</u>. Here's the theory...

1) Initially, all the matter in the universe occupied <u>a very small space</u>. This tiny space was very <u>dense</u> (p.38) and so was very <u>hot</u>.

2) Then it '<u>exploded</u>' — space started expanding, and the <u>expansion</u> is still going on.

New Evidence Might Change Our Theories

1) Something important to remember is that the Big Bang theory is the best guess we have <u>so far</u>. Whenever scientists discover <u>new evidence</u>, they have to either make a <u>new theory</u> or <u>change</u> a current one to <u>explain</u> what they've observed.

2) There is still <u>lots</u> we don't know about the universe. <u>Observations of supernovae</u> from 1998 to the present day appear to show that <u>distant galaxies</u> are moving away from us <u>faster</u> and <u>faster</u> (the <u>speed</u> at which they're receding is <u>increasing</u>).

3) Currently scientists think the universe is mostly made up of <u>dark matter</u> and <u>dark energy</u>. Dark matter is the name given to an <u>unknown substance</u> which holds galaxies <u>together</u>, but does not emit any <u>electromagnetic radiation</u>. Dark energy is thought to be responsible for the <u>accelerated expansion</u> of the universe. But no-one really knows <u>what these things are</u>, so there are lots of different <u>theories</u> about it. These theories get <u>tested</u> over time and are either accepted or rejected.

And it all started with the Big Bang...

Or at least, that's what we currently think is most likely. Remember that theories change depending on evidence.

Q1 How does observed light from distant galaxies suggest that the universe is expanding? [3 marks]

Revision Questions for Topic 8

<u>Topic 8</u> — short, sweet and super interesting. Now it's time to check you filled all that space in your head.

* Try these questions and <u>tick off each one</u> when you <u>get it right</u>.
* When you've done <u>all the questions</u> under a heading and are <u>completely happy</u> with it, tick it off.

The Life Cycle of Stars (p.100) ☑

1) What is a nebula?
2) What causes the rise in temperature that leads to nuclear fusion in a protostar?
3) What causes a main sequence star to remain stable for a long time?
4) What happens to a star about the same size as our Sun when it begins to run out of hydrogen?
5) What is a black dwarf and how is it made?
6) At what stage in a star's life cycle are elements heavier than iron formed?
7) True or false? The Sun will eventually turn into a black hole.

The Solar System and Orbits (p.101) ☑

8) How many stars are there in our solar system?
9) What do planets and dwarf planets orbit?
10) True or false? The moon is an artificial satellite.
11) What galaxy is our solar system part of?
12) What is the approximate shape of the planets' orbits around the Sun?
13) True or false? An object in a stable orbit has a continually changing speed.
14) What is the name of the force that pulls an orbiting object towards Earth?
15) State the direction of the orbiting object's instantaneous velocity in relation to this force.
16) How does the strength of a planet's gravitational force change as you get closer to its surface?
17) What happens to the speed of an orbiting object if its orbital radius increases?
   Explain why this happens.

Red-shift and the Big Bang (p.102) ☑

18) What is red-shift?
19) True or false? Very distant galaxies are moving away faster than ones closer to us.
20) Give two limitations to the balloon model of the expanding universe.
21) Briefly describe the ideas that make up the Big Bang theory.
22) What did scientists discover about the movement of galaxies in 1998 and how did they discover this?
23) True or false? New evidence that disproves a popular theory is ignored.

Apparatus and Techniques

Get your lab coat on, it's time to find out about the skills you'll need in <u>experiments</u>.
First things first — make sure you're using <u>appropriate equipment</u> and know <u>how to use it</u> correctly.

Mass Should Be Measured Using a Balance

1) For a <u>solid</u>, set the balance to <u>zero</u> and then place your object onto the scale and read off the mass.

2) If you're measuring the mass of a <u>liquid</u>, start by putting an empty <u>container</u> onto the <u>balance</u>. Next, <u>reset</u> the balance to zero.

3) Then just pour your <u>liquid</u> into the container and record the mass displayed. Easy peasy.

Measure Most Lengths with a Ruler

1) In most cases a bog-standard <u>centimetre ruler</u> can be used to measure <u>length</u>. It depends on what you're measuring though — <u>metre rulers</u> are handy for <u>large</u> distances, while <u>micrometers</u> are used for measuring tiny things like the <u>diameter of a wire</u>.

2) The ruler should always be <u>parallel to</u> what you want to measure.

3) If you're dealing with something where it's <u>tricky</u> to measure just <u>one</u> accurately (e.g. water ripples, p.74), you can measure the length of <u>ten</u> of them and then <u>divide</u> to find the <u>length of one</u>.

4) If you're taking <u>multiple measurements</u> of the <u>same</u> object (e.g. to measure changes in length) then make sure you always measure from the <u>same point</u> on the object. It can help to draw or stick small <u>markers</u> onto the object to line up your ruler against.

5) Make sure the ruler and the object are always at <u>eye level</u> when you take a reading. This stops <u>parallax</u> affecting your results.

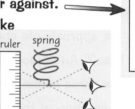

<u>Parallax</u> is where a measurement appears to <u>change</u> based on <u>where you're looking from</u>. The <u>blue line</u> is the measurement taken when the spring is at <u>eye level</u>. It shows the correct length of the spring.

Use a Protractor to Find Angles

1) First align the <u>vertex</u> (point) of the angle with the mark in the <u>centre</u> of the protractor.

2) Line up the <u>base line</u> of the protractor with one line that forms the <u>angle</u> and then measure the angle of the other line using the scale on the <u>protractor</u>.

3) If the lines creating the angle are very <u>thick</u>, align the protractor and measure the angle from the <u>centre</u> of the lines. Using a <u>sharp pencil</u> to trace light rays or draw diagrams helps to <u>reduce errors</u> when measuring angles.

4) If the lines are <u>too short</u> to measure easily, you may have to <u>extend</u> them. Again, make sure you use a <u>sharp pencil</u> to do this.

Measure Temperature Accurately with a Thermometer

1) Make sure the <u>bulb</u> of your thermometer is <u>completely submerged</u> in any substance you're measuring.

2) Wait for the temperature to <u>stabilise</u> before you take your initial reading.

3) Again, read your measurement off the <u>scale</u> on a thermometer at <u>eye level</u>.

When you're reading off a scale, use the value of the nearest mark on the scale (the nearest graduation).

You May Have to Measure the Time Taken for a Change

1) You should use a <u>stopwatch</u> to <u>time</u> most experiments — they're more <u>accurate</u> than regular watches.

2) Always make sure you <u>start</u> and <u>stop</u> the stopwatch at exactly the right time. Or alternatively, set an <u>alarm</u> on the stopwatch so you know exactly when to stop an experiment or take a reading.

3) You might be able to use a <u>light gate</u> instead (p.106). This will <u>reduce the errors</u> in your experiment.

Apparatus and Techniques

Measuring Cylinders and Pipettes Measure Liquid Volume

1) <u>Measuring cylinders</u> are the most common way to measure a liquid.

2) They come in all different <u>sizes</u>. Make sure you choose one that's the <u>right size</u> for the measurement you want to make. It's no good using a huge 1 dm³ cylinder to measure out 2 cm³ of a liquid — the graduations (markings for scale) will be <u>too big</u> and you'll end up with <u>massive errors</u>. It'd be much better to use one that measures up to 10 cm³.

3) You can also use a <u>pipette</u> to measure volume. <u>Pipettes</u> are used to suck up and <u>transfer</u> volumes of liquid between containers.

4) <u>Graduated pipettes</u> are used to transfer <u>accurate</u> volumes. A <u>pipette filler</u> is attached to the end of a graduated pipette, to <u>control</u> the amount of liquid being drawn up.

5) Whichever method you use, always read the volume from the <u>bottom of the meniscus</u> (the curved upper surface of the liquid) when it's at <u>eye level</u>.

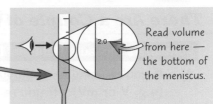

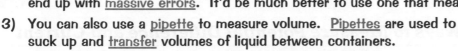

Read volume from here — the bottom of the meniscus.

Eureka Cans Measure the Volumes of Solids

1) <u>Eureka cans</u> are used in <u>combination</u> with <u>measuring cylinders</u> to find the volumes of <u>irregular solids</u> (p.38)

2) They're essentially a <u>beaker with a spout</u>. To use them, fill them with water so the water level is <u>above the spout</u>.

3) Let the water <u>drain</u> from the spout, leaving the water level <u>just below</u> the start of the spout (so <u>all</u> the water displaced by an object goes into the measuring cylinder and gives you the <u>correct volume</u>).

4) Place a <u>measuring cylinder</u> below the end of the spout. When you place a solid in the beaker, it causes the water level to <u>rise</u> and water to flow out of the spout.

5) Make sure you wait until the spout has <u>stopped dripping</u> before you measure the volume of the water in the measuring cylinder. And eureka! You know the object's volume.

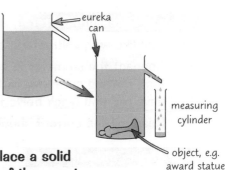

eureka can

measuring cylinder

object, e.g. award statue

Be Careful When You Do Experiments

1) There are always hazards in any experiment, so <u>before</u> you start an experiment you should read and follow any <u>safety precautions</u> to do with your method or the apparatus you're using.

2) Stop masses and equipment falling by using <u>clamp stands</u>. Make sure masses are of a <u>sensible weight</u> so they don't break the equipment they're used with, and use <u>pulleys</u> of a sensible <u>length</u>. That way, any hanging masses won't <u>hit the floor</u> during the experiment.

3) When <u>heating</u> materials, make sure to let them <u>cool</u> before moving them, or wear <u>insulated gloves</u> while handling them. If you're using an <u>immersion heater</u> to heat liquids, you should always let it <u>dry out</u> in air, just in case any liquid has leaked inside the heater.

4) If you're using a <u>laser</u>, there are a few safety rules you must follow. Always wear <u>laser safety goggles</u> and never <u>look directly into</u> the laser or shine it <u>towards another person</u>. Make sure you turn the laser <u>off</u> if it's not needed to avoid any accidents.

5) When working with electronics, make sure you use a <u>low</u> enough <u>voltage</u> and <u>current</u> to prevent wires <u>overheating</u> (and potentially melting) and avoid <u>damage to components</u>, like blowing a filament bulb.

6) You also need to be aware of <u>general safety</u> in the lab — handle <u>glassware</u> carefully so it doesn't <u>break</u>, don't stick your fingers in sockets and avoid touching frayed wires. That kind of thing.

Experimentus apparatus...

Wizardry won't help you here, unfortunately. Most of this'll be pretty familiar to you by now, but make sure you get your head down and know these techniques inside out so they're second nature when it comes to any practicals.

Working with Electronics

Electrical devices are used in a bunch of experiments, so make sure you know how to use them.

You Have to Interpret Circuit Diagrams

Before you get cracking on an experiment involving any kind of electrical devices, you have to plan and build your circuit using a circuit diagram. Make sure you know all of the circuit symbols on page 24 so you're not stumped before you've even started.

There Are a Couple of Ways to Measure Potential Difference and Current

Voltmeters Measure Potential Difference

1) If you're using an analogue voltmeter, choose the voltmeter with the most appropriate unit (e.g. V or mV). If you're using a digital voltmeter, you'll most likely be able to switch between them.

2) Connect the voltmeter in parallel (p.25) across the component you want to test. The wires that come with a voltmeter are usually red (positive) and black (negative). These go into the red and black coloured ports on the voltmeter. Funnily enough.

3) Then simply read the potential difference from the scale (or from the screen if it's digital).

Ammeters Measure Current

1) Just like with voltmeters, choose the ammeter with the most appropriate unit.

2) Connect the ammeter in series (p.25) with the component you want to test, making sure they're both on the same branch. Again, they usually have red and black ports to show you where to connect your wires.

3) Read off the current shown on the scale or by the screen.

> Turn your circuit off between readings to prevent wires heating up and affecting your results (p.26).

Multimeters Measure Both

1) Instead of having a separate ammeter and voltmeter, many circuits use multimeters. These are devices that measure a range of properties — usually potential difference, current and resistance.

2) If you want to find potential difference, make sure the red wire is plugged into the port that has a 'V' (for volts).

3) To find the current, use the port labelled 'A' or 'mA' (for amps).

4) The dial on the multimeter should then be turned to the relevant section, e.g. to 'A' to measure current in amps. The screen will display the value you're measuring.

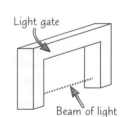

Light Gates Measure Speed and Acceleration

1) A light gate sends a beam of light from one side of the gate to a detector on the other side. When something passes through the gate, the beam of light is interrupted. The light gate then measures how long the beam was undetected.

2) To find the speed of an object, connect the light gate to a computer. Measure the length of the object and input this using the software. It will then automatically calculate the speed of the object as it passes through the beam.

3) To measure acceleration, use an object that interrupts the signal twice in a short period of time, e.g. a piece of card with a gap cut into the middle.

4) The light gate measures the speed for each section of the object and uses this to calculate its acceleration. This can then be read from the computer screen.

Have a look at page 66 for an example of a light gate being used.

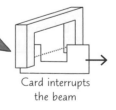

Light gate

Beam of light

Card interrupts the beam

A light gate is better than a heavy one...

After finishing this page, you should be able to take on any electrical experiment that they throw at you... ouch.

Answers

Page 11 — Energy Stores and Systems
Q1 Energy is transferred mechanically *[1 mark]* from the kinetic energy store of the wind *[1 mark]* to the kinetic energy store of the windmill *[1 mark]*.

Page 12 — Kinetic and Potential Energy Stores
Q1 The change in height is 5.0 m. So the energy transferred from the gravitational potential energy store is:
$E_p = mgh = 2.0 \times 9.8 \times 5.0 = 98$ J *[1 mark]*
This is transferred to the kinetic energy store of the object, so $E_k = 98$ J *[1 mark]*
$E_k = \frac{1}{2}mv^2$ so $v^2 = 2E_k \div m$ *[1 mark]*
$= (2 \times 98) \div 2.0$ *[1 mark]*
$= 98$ m²/s²
$v = \sqrt{98} = 9.899...$
$= 9.9$ m/s (to 2 s.f.) *[1 mark]*

Page 13 — Specific Heat Capacity
Q1 $\Delta E = mc\Delta\theta$ so $\Delta\theta = \Delta E \div (m \times c)$ *[1 mark]*
$= 50\ 000 \div (5 \times 4200) = 2.4$ °C *[1 mark]*
So the new temperature
$= 5 + 2.4 = 7.4$ °C *[1 mark]*

Page 14 — Conservation of Energy and Power
Q1 $P = E \div t$
$t = 2 \times 60 = 120$ s *[1 mark]*
$P = 4800 \div 120$ *[1 mark]* $= 40$ W *[1 mark]*

Page 15 — Conduction and Convection
Q1 Heating transfers energy to the particle's kinetic energy stores *[1 mark]*. These particles vibrate and transfer energy between them — gradually transferring the energy through the solid *[1 mark]*. This is called conduction *[1 mark]*

Page 16 — Reducing Unwanted Energy Transfers
Q1 Cavity wall insulation reduces energy transfer by convection *[1 mark]*. It also reduces energy transfer by conduction *[1 mark]* because the insulating foam has a low thermal conductivity and so has a low rate of energy transfer from thermal energy stores *[1 mark]*.

Page 17 — Efficiency
Q1 efficiency = useful output energy transfer
$\div$ total input energy transfer
$= 225 \div 300$ *[1 mark]* $= 0.75$ *[1 mark]*
Q2 efficiency = useful power output
$\div$ total power input
$= 900 \div 1200 = 0.75$ *[1 mark]*
useful output energy transfer
= efficiency × total input energy transfer
[1 mark]
$= 0.75 \times 72\ 000$ *[1 mark]* $= 54\ 000$ J *[1 mark]*

Page 18 — Energy Resources and their Uses
Q1 a) renewable *[1 mark]*
b) non-renewable *[1 mark]*
c) non-renewable *[1 mark]*
d) renewable *[1 mark]*

Page 19 — Wind, Solar and Geothermal
Q1 E.g. wind power can be unreliable as sometimes there's no wind or the turbines have to be stopped because the wind is too strong, so they don't provide a constant supply of energy *[1 mark]*. Geothermal power plants can run continuously as they transfer energy from the thermal energy store of the ground *[1 mark]*.

Page 20 — Hydro-electricity, Waves and Tides
Q1 E.g. they disturb the seabed / they disturb the habitats of marine animals *[1 mark]*

Page 21 — Bio-fuels and Non-renewables
Q1 Any two from: e.g. they're reliable / they're comparatively cheap to run / they can respond quickly to changes in demand *[2 marks]*
Q2 E.g. burning oil releases carbon dioxide, which contributes to global warming *[1 mark]*. It also produces sulfur dioxide which causes acid rain, which is harmful to trees and animals and can have far-reaching effects in ecosystems *[1 mark]*. Oil spills also occur when transporting oil, which can harm/kill animals that live in and around the sea *[1 mark]*.

Page 22 — Trends in Energy Resource Use
Q1 Any two from: e.g. building new power plants is expensive / people don't want to live near new power plants / renewable energy resources are less reliable than non-renewable energy resources / hybrid cars are more expensive than equivalent petrol cars *[2 marks]*.

Page 24 — Current and Circuit Symbols
Q1 $Q = It$ so $t = Q \div I$ *[1 mark]*
$= 28\ 800 \div 8.0$ *[1 mark]*
$= 3600$ s (= 1 hour) *[1 mark]*
Q2 E.g.

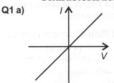

[1 mark for each correct symbol connected in a single loop, otherwise, award 2 marks for correct symbols in an incorrect loop]

Page 25 — Resistance and V = IR
Q1 $V = IR$ so $R = V \div I$ *[1 mark]*
$= 230 \div 5$ *[1 mark]* $= 46\ \Omega$ *[1 mark]*

Page 26 — Resistance and I-V Characteristics
Q1 a)

[1 mark for correct axes, 1 mark for a straight line through the origin]
b)

[1 mark for correct axes, 1 mark for correct shape]

Page 27 — Circuit Devices
Q1 a) E.g. automatic night lights — a light automatically turns on when it gets dark *[1 mark]*.
b) E.g. thermostats — the heating automatically turns on/off at a certain temperature *[1 mark]*.

Page 28 — Series Circuits
Q1 $V = 12 + 12 = 24$ V *[1 mark]*
$R = 2 + 3 + 7 = 12\ \Omega$ *[1 mark]*
$V = I \times R$ so $I = V \div R$ *[1 mark]*
$= 24 \div 12$ *[1 mark]* $= 2$ A *[1 mark]*

Page 29 — Parallel Circuits
Q1 The current through the circuit increases *[1 mark]* and the total resistance of the circuit decreases to less than the resistance of the smallest resistor *[1 mark]*.

Page 30 — Investigating Resistance
Q1

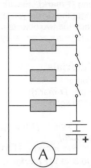

[1 mark for a circuit with several resistors connected in parallel and switches allowing one resistor to be added at a time.]

Page 31 — Electricity in the Home
Q1 a) 230 V *[1 mark]*
b) 0 V *[1 mark]*
c) 0 V *[1 mark]*

Page 32 — Power of Electrical Appliances
Q1 $P = E \div t = 6000 \div 30$ *[1 mark]*
$= 200$ W *[1 mark]*
Q2 $P = E \div t$ so $E = P \times t$ *[1 mark]*
$= 250 \times (2 \times 60 \times 60)$
$= 1\ 800\ 000$ J *[1 mark]*
$E = 375 \times (2 \times 60 \times 60) = 2\ 700\ 000$ J *[1 mark]*
So change in energy is
$2\ 700\ 000 - 1\ 800\ 000 = 900\ 000$ J *[1 mark]*

Page 33 — More on Power
Q1 $E = Q \times V = 10\ 000 \times 200$ *[1 mark]*
$= 2\ 000\ 000$ J *[1 mark]*
Q2 $P = V \times I = 12 \times 4.0$ *[1 mark]* $= 48$ W *[1 mark]*
Q3 $P = V \times I = 230 \times 10.0 = 2300$ W *[1 mark]*
This is equal to $P = I^2R$ *[1 mark]*
$R = P \div I^2$ *[1 mark]* $= 2300 \div 10.0^2$ *[1 mark]*
$= 23\ \Omega$ *[1 mark]*

Page 34 — The National Grid
Q1 The National Grid distributes electricity at a high pd and a low current *[1 marks]*. A high pd means that it can distribute lots of power per second (as power = pd × current) *[1 mark]*. Using a low current reduces energy losses *[1 mark]* which makes the National Grid efficient at transferring energy *[1 mark]*.

Page 35 — Static Electricity
Q1 As the jumper rubs against his shirt, a static charge builds up on the both the jumper and the shirt *[1 mark]*. This is due to electrons being removed from one and being deposited onto the other *[1 mark]*. The charge becomes large enough for electrons to 'jump' across the small air gap between the jumper and the shirt, causing sparks *[1 mark]*.

Page 29 — Parallel Circuits
Q2 E.g.

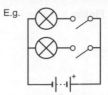

[1 mark for the correct circuit symbols, 1 mark for two bulbs connected in parallel, 1 mark for both switches being on the same branches as the lamps]

Answers

Page 36 — Electric Fields

Q1

[1 mark for lines at a right angle to the surface, 1 mark for lines pointing away from the sphere]

Q2 The force between the charges increases as they get closer together *[1 mark]* This is because the force is caused by the electric fields of the charges interacting *[1 mark]*. Electric field strength gets stronger the closer you get to a charged object, so when the two objects are closer together the field is stronger and they feel a larger force *[1 mark]*.

Page 38 — Density of Materials

Q1 First find the cube's volume:
$1.5 \times 1.5 \times 1.5 = 3.375$ cm³ *[1 mark]*
The cube's density is 3500 kg/m³.
1 g/cm³ = 1000 kg/m³,
so this is 3500 ÷ 1000 = 3.5 g/cm³ *[1 mark]*.
$\rho = mV$ so $m = \rho \times V$ *[1 mark]*
$= 3.5 \times 3.375$ *[1 mark]* = 11.8125
= 11.8 g (to 3 s.f.) *[1 mark]*.

Page 39 — Internal Energy and Changes of State

Q1 Heating the solid transfers energy to the kinetic energy stores of the particles (increasing the internal energy) *[1 mark]*. When the particles have enough energy in their kinetic energy stores, they can break the bonds holding them together *[1 mark]*. The solid changes state and becomes liquid *[1 mark]*.

Page 40 — Specific Latent Heat

Q1 $E = m \times L = 0.25 \times 120\ 000$ *[1 mark]*
$= 30\ 000$ J *[1 mark]*

Page 41 — Particle Motion in Gases

Q1 pV = constant, so when
$V = 3.5$ m³, $pV = 520 \times 3.5$
= 1820 *[1 mark]*
When $V = 1$ m³, $p \times 1 = 1820$ *[1 mark]*,
so $p = 1820$ Pa *[1 mark]*

Page 43 — Developing the Model of the Atom

Q1 a) The centre of an atom is a tiny, positively charged nucleus *[1 mark]*. This is made up of protons and neutrons and is the source of most of the atom's mass *[1 mark]*. Most of the atom is empty space *[1 mark]*. Electrons orbit the nucleus at set energy levels *[1 mark]*.

b) The radius of an atom is around 1×10^{-10} m *[1 mark]*. The radius of a nucleus is 10 000 times smaller than this *[1 mark]*.

Page 44 — Isotopes and Nuclear Radiation

Q1 E.g. Alpha would not be suitable because it is stopped by a few cm of air or a sheet of paper *[1 mark]*. It would not be able to pass through the packaging to sterilise the equipment *[1 mark]*.

Page 45 — Nuclear Equations

Q1 Beta particles *[1 mark]*

Q2 $^{219}_{86}Rn \rightarrow {}^{215}_{84}Po + {}^{4}_{2}He$
[1 mark for correct layout, 1 mark for correct symbol for an alpha particle, 1 mark for total atomic and mass numbers being equal on both sides]

Page 46 — Half-life

Q1 After one half-life the count-rate will be
40 ÷ 2 = 20 cps *[1 mark]*
After a second: 20 ÷ 2 = 10 cps
After a third: 10 ÷ 2 = 5 cps *[1 mark]*
So the ratio is 5:40 = 1:8 *[1 mark]*

Page 47 — Background Radiation and Contamination

Q1 E.g. rocks *[1 mark]*, cosmic rays *[1 mark]* and fallout from nuclear explosions *[1 mark]*

Page 48 — Uses and Risk

Q1 Gamma rays are directed carefully at a tumour *[1 mark]*. Because a high dose of gamma rays will kill living cells, the cancerous cells will be destroyed without damaging too many normal healthy cells *[1 mark]*.

Q2 a) Radioactive isotopes are swallowed by or injected into a person *[1 mark]*. The radiation the isotope gives off is detected and a computer shows where the strongest readings are coming from to show how the body is working *[1 mark]*.

b) Medical tracers use radiation and this poses a risk to the human body, e.g. it can cause damage or mutation of cells *[1 mark]*. Patients may think these risks are too serious and want other tests to be performed instead *[1 mark]*.

Page 49 — Fission and Fusion

Q1 a) A large and unstable nucleus absorbs a neutron *[1 mark]*. This causes it to split into two roughly equal sized nuclei *[1 mark]*. Two or three neutrons are also released when the large nucleus splits *[1 mark]*. The energy not transferred to the smaller nuclei or neutrons is transferred to the surroundings by gamma rays *[1 mark]*.

b)

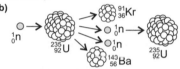

[1 mark for a neutron being absorbed to cause splitting, 1 mark for a large nucleus splitting into two smaller nuclei, 1 mark for it producing a neutron that is absorbed by another large, unstable nucleus]

Page 51— Contact and Non-Contact Forces

Q1 Contact force: air resistance *[1 mark]*
Non-contact force: gravitational force *[1 mark]*

Q2 a) Any two from: e.g. speed / distance / mass / temperature *[2 marks]*

b) Any two from: e.g. displacement / momentum / force / acceleration / velocity *[2 marks]*

Page 52 — Weight, Mass and Gravity

Q1 a) $W = mg = 5 \times 9.8$ *[1 mark]* = 49 N *[1 mark]*

b) $W = 5 \times 1.6$ *[1 mark]* = 8 N *[1 mark]*

Page 53 — Resultant Forces and Work Done

Q1 20 cm = 0.2 m *[1 mark]*
$W = Fs = 20 \times 0.2$ *[1 mark]* = 4 J *[1 mark]*

Page 54 — Calculating Forces

Q1

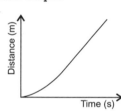

Resultant = 13 N
[1 mark for a correct scale drawing, 1 mark for correct resultant force]

Page 55 — Forces and Elasticity

Q1 2 cm = 0.02 m *[1 mark]*
$F = ke$ so $k = F \div e$ *[1 mark]*
$= 1 \div 0.02$
= 50 N/m *[1 mark]*

Page 56 — Investigating Springs

Q1 2.5 cm = 0.025 m *[1 mark]*
$E_e = \frac{1}{2}ke^2 = \frac{1}{2} \times 40 \times (0.025)^2$ *[1 mark]*
= 0.0125 J *[1 mark]*

Page 57 — Moments

Q1 For forces to balance, anticlockwise moment = clockwise moment *[1 mark]*
Let your distance = y
So $300 \times 2 = 600 \times y$ *[1 mark]*
$y = 600 \div 600 = 1$ m *[1 mark]*

Page 58 — Fluid Pressure

Q1 $p = F \div A$ so $F = p \times A$ *[1 mark]*
$= 200\ 000 \times 10$ *[1 mark]*
$= 2\ 000\ 000$ N *[1 mark]*

Q2 $p = h\rho g$ so $\rho = p \div hg$ *[1 mark]*
$\rho = 450 \div (0.050 \times 9.8)$ *[1 mark]*
$\rho = 918.36... = 920$ kg/m³ (to 2 s.f.) *[1 mark]*

Page 59 — Upthrust and Atmospheric Pressure

Q1 Wood is less dense than water *[1 mark]*, which means that when a wooden object is placed in water, it can displace enough water to create an upthrust equal to the weight of the object *[1 mark]*. So the upthrust equals the weight and it floats *[1 mark]*.

Page 60 — Distance, Displacement, Speed and Velocity

Q1 $s = vt$ so $v = s \div t$ *[1 mark]*
$= 200 \div 25$ *[1 mark]* = 8 m/s *[1 mark]*

Q2 a) Distance travelled = 1500 m *[1 mark]*

b) Marie's journey ends at the same position as it started, so the displacement is 0 m *[1 mark]*.

Page 61 — Acceleration

Q1 $u = 0$ m/s, $v = 7$ m/s, $a = g = 9.8$ m/s²,
$s = (v^2 - u^2) \div 2a$ *[1 mark]*
$= (49 - 0) \div (2 \times 9.8)$ *[1 mark]*
= 2.5 m *[1 mark]*

Page 62 — Distance-Time and Velocity-Time Graphs

Q1 E.g.

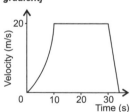

[1 mark for a curved line with an increasing positive gradient, 1 mark for the line becoming a straight line with a positive gradient]

Q2

[1 mark for an upwards curved acceleration line to 20m/s, 1 mark for a straight line representing steady speed, 1 mark for a straight line representing deceleration]

Page 63 — Terminal Velocity

Q1 As the ball falls, it accelerates towards earth due to the force of gravity *[1 mark]*. Air resistance also acts on the ball, in the opposite direction to the force due to gravity *[1 mark]*. As the ball speeds up, the air resistance increases until the accelerating force and the air resistance balance *[1 mark]*. The object cannot go any faster — this is its terminal velocity *[1 mark]*.

Page 64 — Newton's First and Second Laws

Q1 $F = ma = (80 + 10) \times 0.25$ *[1 mark]*
= 22.5 N *[1 mark]*

Answers

Page 65 — Inertia and Newton's Third Law

Q1 When you lean on a wall, you exert a force on the wall. Due to Newton's Third Law, the wall also exerts an equal but opposite force (normal contact force) back on you *[1 mark]*. You also exert a force on the ground and the ground exerts a force on you *[1 mark]*. The resultant force is zero so you remain stationary *[1 mark]*.

Page 66 — Investigating Motion

Q1 A piece of card with a gap in the middle is attached to the trolley, so that two bits of card stick up and interrupt the light gate beam as it moves *[1 mark]*. The length of each bit of card is input into the light gate software, and the light gate measures the velocity of each bit of card as the trolley moves *[1 mark]*. It can use the two velocity values to find the acceleration *[1 mark]*.

Page 67 — Stopping Distances

Q1 Any one from: e.g. speed / road surface / condition of tyres / condition of brakes *[1 mark]*

Page 68 — Reaction Times

Q1 a) $v^2 - u^2 = 2as$
$v^2 = 2 \times 9.8 \times 0.162 + 0$ *[1 mark]* = 3.1752
$v = \sqrt{3.1752} = 1.781...$ m/s *[1 mark]*
$a = \Delta v \div t$ so
$t = \Delta v \div a$ *[1 mark]*
= 1.781... ÷ 9.8 *[1 mark]* = 0.181... s
= 0.18 s (to 2 s.f.) *[1 mark]*

b) His reaction time is longer in the evening *[1 mark]* so whilst driving, he may take longer to react to a hazard, meaning his thinking distance would be longer *[1 mark]*.

Page 69 — More on Stopping Distances

Q1 Thinking distance increases linearly with speed, so thinking distance = 3 × 6 = 18 m *[1 mark]*
Braking distance increases with speed by 3^2 times.
So braking distance = $3^2 \times 6$ *[1 mark]*
= 54 m *[1 mark]*
Stopping distance = 18 + 54 = 72 m *[1 mark]*

Page 70 — Momentum

Q1 $p = mv = 60 \times 3$ *[1 mark]* = 180 kg m/s *[1 mark]*

Q2 Before the gun fires the bullet, the total momentum is zero (neither the gun nor the bullet are moving) *[1 mark]*. When the bullet leaves the gun, it has momentum in one direction *[1 mark]*. The gun moves backwards so it has momentum in the opposite direction *[1 mark]*. This means that the total momentum after the bullet has been fired is zero. Momentum has been conserved *[1 mark]*.

Page 71 — Changes in Momentum

Q1 $p_{before} = (10 \times 6) + (20 \times 0) = 60$ kg m/s *[1 mark]*
$p_{after} = (10 + 20) \times v = 30v$ *[1 mark]*
$p_{before} = p_{after}$
$60 = 30v$
so $v = 60 \div 30 = 2$ m/s *[1 mark]*

Page 73 — Transverse and Longitudinal Waves

Q1 7.5 ÷ 100 = 0.075 m *[1 mark]*
wave speed = frequency × wavelength, so frequency = wave speed ÷ wavelength *[1 mark]*
= 0.15 ÷ 0.075 *[1 mark]*
= 2 Hz *[1 mark]*

Page 74 — Experiments With Waves

Q1 E.g. attach a signal generator to a dipper and place it in a ripple tank filled with water to create some waves *[1 mark]*. Place a screen underneath the ripple tank, then turn on a lamp above the tank and dim the other lights in the room *[1 mark]*. Measure the distance between shadow lines that are 10 wavelengths apart on the screen beneath the tank, then divide this number by 10 — this is equal to the wavelength of the ripples *[1 mark]*.

Page 75 — Reflection

Q1 Specular reflection *[1 mark]*

Q2

[1 mark for correct diagram showing rays and the normal, 1 mark for correct angle of incidence, 1 mark for correct angle of reflection]

Page 76 — Electromagnetic Waves and Refraction

Q1

[1 mark for a correct diagram showing rays and the normal, 1 mark for an angle of incidence of 40°, 1 mark for an angle of refraction greater than 40°]

Page 77 — Investigating Light

Q1 a) Draw around a glass block onto a piece of paper. Shine a light ray from a ray box into the block *[1 mark]*. Trace the incident ray and mark where the ray emerges from the block. Remove the block and join these up with a straight line *[1 mark]*. Measure the angle of incidence and angle of refraction *[1 mark]*. Repeat this experiment for different materials, keeping the angle of incidence constant and seeing how the angle of refraction changes with the material *[1 mark]*.

b) So you can easily trace the light ray to measure the angle between the ray and the normal *[1 mark]*.

Page 78 — Radio Waves

Q1 E.g. hands-free Bluetooth® headsets to use in the car *[1 mark]*.

Q2 Radio waves can be produced by alternating currents / oscillations of charged particles in electrical circuits *[1 mark]*.

Page 79 — EM Waves and Their Uses

Q1 They can pass easily through the Earth's watery atmosphere without being absorbed *[1 mark]*.

Page 80 — More Uses of EM Waves

Q1 E.g. X-ray photographs *[1 mark]* treating cancer (radiotherapy) *[1 mark]*

Q2 Visible light is not easily absorbed or scattered in a fibre *[1 mark]*.

Page 81 — Dangers of Electromagnetic Waves

Q1 Any two from: e.g. UV radiation damages surface cells / cause sunburn / cause premature ageing of the skin / cause blindness / increase the risk of skin cancer.
[2 marks — 1 mark for each correct effect]

Q2 7 mSv ÷ 0.7 mSv = 10
So the added risk of harm from a CT scan is ten times higher than from an X-ray *[1 mark]*.

Page 82 — Lenses

Q1 a) The point where rays hitting the lens parallel to the axis meet *[1 mark]*

b) The point where light rays hitting the lens parallel to the axis appear to come from *[1 mark]*

Q2

[1 mark for parallel lines being refracted and brought together as they pass through the lens, 1 mark for lines meeting at the principal focus (F)]

Page 83 — Images and Ray Diagrams

Q1

[1 mark for an image at a distance 2F in front of the lens, 1 mark for an inverted image, 1 mark for two correct light rays]

Page 84 — Concave Lenses and Magnification

Q1 magnification = image height ÷ object height
= 6 ÷ 12 *[1 mark]* = 0.5 *[1 mark]*

Q2 magnification = image height ÷ object height so image height = magnification × object height *[1 mark]*
= 2.5 × 10 *[1 mark]* = 25 cm *[1 mark]*

Page 85 — Visible Light

Q1 The red bag is only reflecting red light and the green buckle is only reflecting green light. All other wavelengths of visible light are absorbed *[1 mark]*. Colour filters only allow wavelengths that match their colour through, so the filter will only let through green light *[1 mark]*. This means that the buckle will appear green, as the light reflected by it can pass through the filter *[1 mark]*. However, the red bag will appear black, because the filter doesn't allow through the red light being reflected by the bag *[1 mark]*.

Page 86 — Infrared Radiation and Temperature

Q1 The bowl of ice cream is absorbing more radiation than it is emitting *[1 mark]*. This causes an increase in the temperature of the bowl of ice cream *[1 mark]*.

Page 87 — Black Body Radiation

Q1 The Sun is hotter *[1 mark]*. The hotter an object it is, the shorter its peak wavelength *[1 mark]*

Page 88 — Sound Waves

Q1 Air particles are moving back and forth, creating pressure on your ear drum *[1 mark]*. This change in pressure causes the ear drum to vibrate *[1 mark]*. These vibrations pass from your ear drum to the inside of your ear *[1 mark]*. These vibrations are turned into electrical signals, which are sent to your brain so you can hear the sound *[1 mark]*.

Page 89 — Ultrasound

Q1 $s = vt$
Time taken for sound to reach the seabed:
$t = s \div v$ *[1 mark]* = 2500 ÷ 1520
= 1.64... *[1 mark]*
Time taken for the sound to return:
1.64... × 2 = 3.28... = 3.3 s (to 2 s.f.) *[1 mark]*

Page 90 — Exploring Structures Using Waves

Q1 The S-waves can't travel though the centre of the Earth, so at least part of the Earth's core must be liquid *[1 mark]*. S-waves can only travel through solids *[1 mark]*.

Page 92 — Permanent and Induced Magnets

Q1

[1 mark for a correct diagram, 1 mark for an indication of the field being strongest at the poles]

Answers

Q2 E.g. permanent magnets produce their own magnetic fields but induced magnets become magnets when they're in a magnetic field *[1 mark]*. The force between an induced magnet and a permanent magnet is always attractive, but between two permanent magnets it can be attractive or repulsive *[1 mark]*.

Page 93 — Electromagnetism

Q1 a) E.g. for current out of the Page:

[1 mark for concentric circles getting further apart, 1 mark for arrows on field lines with correct direction]

b)

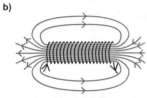

[1 mark for uniform field inside coil, 1 mark for field similar to a bar magnet outside of coil]

Page 94 — The Motor Effect

Q1 a) Into the Page *[1 mark]*

b) 20 cm = 0.2 m *[1 mark]*
$F = BIl = 0.1 \times 8 \times 0.2$ *[1 mark]*
$= 0.16$ N *[1 mark]*

Page 95 — Electric Motors and Loudspeakers

Q1 A coil of wire carrying an alternating current is wrapped around a pole of a permanent magnet which is surrounded by the other pole, then attached to a paper cone *[1 mark]*. When a current flows through the wire, this causes a force which moves the cone in one direction *[1 mark]*. When the current reverses, the force is reversed and the cone is moved in the opposite direction *[1 mark]*. This makes the cone vibrate, which vibrates the air around it to create a sound wave, of the same frequency as the alternating current *[1 mark]*.

Page 96 — The Generator Effect

Q1 The induction of a potential difference (and a current if there is a complete circuit) in a wire which is moving relative to a magnetic field, or experiencing a change in magnetic field *[1 mark]*.

Q2 Increase the speed of the movement *[1 mark]*. Increase the strength of the magnetic field *[1 mark]*.

Page 97 — Generators and Microphones

Q1 a)

[1 mark for correct axes, 1 mark for correct line]

b) A coil is made to rotate in a magnetic field *[1 mark]*. This induces a potential difference across the coil, which causes a current to flow through it *[1 mark]*. A split-ring commutator is used to swap the connection each half turn to keep the current flowing in the same direction *[1 mark]*.

Page 98 — Transformers

Q1 a) $V_p \div V_s = n_p \div n_s$
$V_p = (n_p \div n_s) \times V_s$ *[1 mark]*
$= (16 \div 4) \times 20$ *[1 mark]* $= 80$ V *[1 mark]*

b) output power = input power
$P = VI$ so $V_s \times I_s = V_p \times I_p$
$320 = 80 \times I_p$ *[1 mark]*
$I_p = 320 \div 80$ *[1 mark]* $= 4$ A *[1 mark]*

Page 100 — The Life Cycle of Stars

Q1 E.g. When the star runs out of hydrogen to fuse, it will expand and cool, becoming a red super giant *[1 mark]*. It begins to glow brightly again and expands and contracts several times until it explodes in a supernova *[1 mark]*. The supernova throws dust and gas into space and leaves behind a very dense core called a neutron star *[1 mark]*. This will become a black hole if it is massive enough *[1 mark]*.

Page 101 — The Solar System and Orbits

Q1 E.g. artificial satellites are made by humans, whilst natural satellites are not *[1 mark]*.

Q2 Its orbital speed would be faster *[1 mark]*. The force due to gravity increases the closer you get to the Earth's surface *[1 mark]*. So if the radius of the Moon's orbit was smaller, a larger centripetal force would be acting on it *[1 mark]*. So to remain in a stable orbit, the Moon's instantaneous velocity would need to be larger *[1 mark]*.

Page 102 — Red-shift and the Big Bang

Q1 Observed light from galaxies has all been red-shifted *[1 mark]*. This suggests that the light sources (the distant galaxies) are moving away from us *[1 mark]*. Observations have shown that these distant galaxies are moving away from us at an increasing speed. This supports the idea that space is expanding, causing the distances between galaxies to increase *[1 mark]*.

Index

Index